SRA
Real Math

Stephen S. Willoughby

•

Carl Bereiter

•

Peter Hilton

•

Joseph H. Rubinstein

•

Joan Moss

•

Jean Pedersen

Columbus, OH

The McGraw·Hill Companies

Authors

Stephen S. Willoughby
Professor Emeritus of Mathematics
University of Arizona
Tucson, AZ

Carl Bereiter
Professor Emeritus
Centre for Applied Cognitive Science
Ontario Institute for Studies in Education
University of Toronto, Canada

Peter Hilton
Distinguished Professor of
Mathematics Emeritus
State University of New York
Binghamton, NY

Joseph H. Rubinstein
Professor of Education
Coker College, SC
Hartsville, SC

Joan Moss
Assistant Professor, Department of Human
Development and Applied Psychology
Ontario Institute for Studies in Education
University of Toronto, Canada

Jean Pedersen
Professor, Department of
Mathematics and Computer Science
Santa Clara University, Santa Clara, CA

PreKindergarten and Building Blocks Authors

Douglas H. Clements
Professor of Early Childhood and Mathematics Education
University at Buffalo
State University of New York, NY

Julie Sarama
Associate Professor of Mathematics Education
University at Buffalo
State University of New York, NY

Contributing Authors

Hortensia Soto-Johnson
Assistant Professor of Mathematics
University of Northern Colorado, CO

Erika Walker
Assistant Professor of Mathematics and Education
Teachers College, Columbia University, NY

Research Consultants

Jeremy Kilpatrick
Regents Professor of Mathematics Education
University of Georgia, GA

Alfinio Flores
Professor of Mathematics Education
Arizona State University, AZ

Gilbert J. Cuevas
Professor of Mathematics Education
University of Miami, Coral Gables, FL

Contributing Writers

Holly MacLean, Ed.D., Supervisor Principal, Treasure Valley
Mathematics and Science Center, Boise, ID
Edward Manfre, Mathematics Education Consultant, Albuquerque, NM
Elizabeth Jimenez, English Language Learner Consultant, Pomona, CA

Kim L. Pettig, Ed.D., Instructional Challenge Coordinator
Pittsford Central School District, Pittsford, NY
Rosemary Tolliver, M.Ed., Gifted Coordinator/Curriculum Director, Columbus, OH

National Advisory Board

Justin Anderson, Teacher, Robey Elementary School, Indianapolis, IN
David S. Bradley, Administrator, Granite UT
Donna M. Bradley, Head of the Lower School, St. Marks Episcopal
Palm Beach Gardens, FL
Grace Dublin, Teacher, Laurelhurst Elementary, Seattle, WA
Leisha W. Fordham, Teacher, Bolton Academy, Atlanta, GA

Ebony Frierson, Teacher, Eastminister Day School, Columbia, SC
Flavia Gunter, Teacher, Morningside Elementary School, Atlanta, GA
Audrey Marie Jacobs, Teacher, Lewis & Clark Elementary, St. Louis, MO
Florencetine Jasmin, Elementary Math Curriculum Specialist, Baltimore, MD
Kim Leitzke, Teacher, Clara Barton Elementary School, Milwaukee, WI
Nick Restivo, Principal, Long Beach High School, Long Island, NY

SRAonline.com

 SRA

Send all inquiries to:
SRA/McGraw-Hill
8787 Orion Place
Columbus, OH 43240-4027

ISBN 0-07-602997-2

2 3 4 5 6 7 8 9 VHJ 12 11 10 09 08 07 06

The **McGraw·Hill** Companies

Numbers and Patterns

CHAPTER 2 — Organizing Data

Exploring 💡 Problem Solving Theme: Dog Show

Informal Measurement

CHAPTER 3

Exploring 💡 **Problem Solving** Theme: Seashore

CHAPTER 4
Informal Addition and Subtraction

Exploring 💡 Problem Solving Theme: Computer Games

Introducing Addition and Subtraction Facts

CHAPTER 5

Exploring 💡 Problem Solving Theme: Yard Sale

CHAPTER 6
More Addition Facts

Exploring 💡 Problem Solving Theme: Post Office

Exploring 💡 Problem Solving Theme: Aquariums

Exploring 💡 Problem Solving **Theme: Homes**

Geometry

CHAPTER 9

Exploring 💡 Problem Solving   Theme: Buying and Selling

Measurement

Exploring 💡 Problem Solving Theme: Weather

CHAPTER 12

Using Numbers to 100

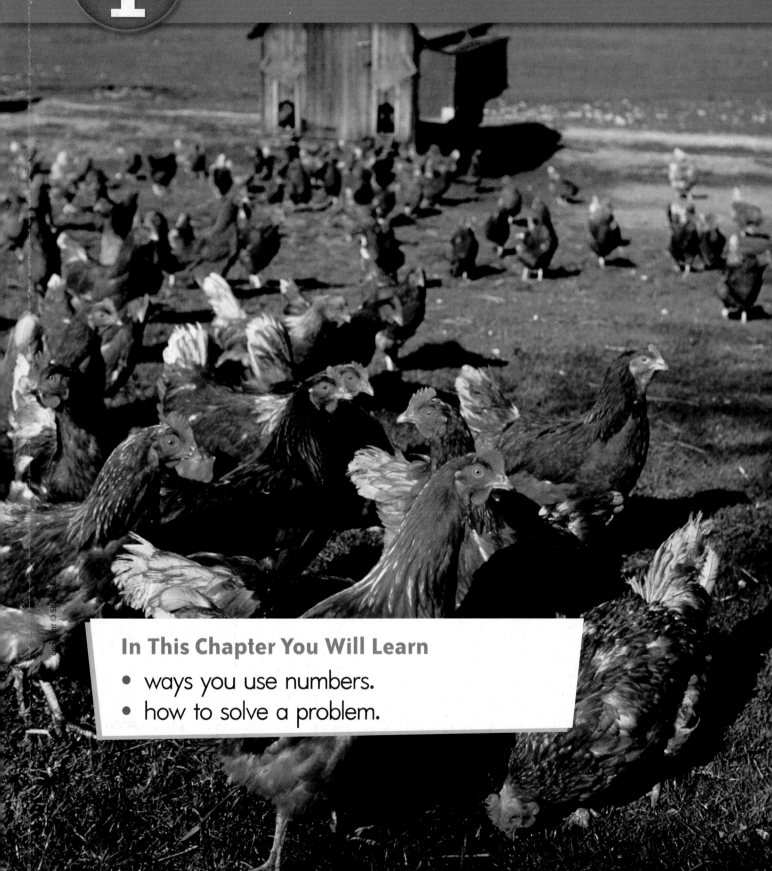

CHAPTER 1 Numbers and Patterns

In This Chapter You Will Learn

- ways you use numbers.
- how to solve a problem.

1

Name _____ Date _____

Listen to the teacher. Work in groups to solve the problems.

LESSON 1.1 Classifying and Counting

Listen. Follow the directions for each picture.

1

2

125E8AFC4

3

 Note to Home Students follow teacher directions for classifying pictures into groups.

Textbook This lesson is available in the **eTextbook.**

3

Listen. Follow the directions for each picture.

4

5

6

7 **Extended Response** How would you classify these objects? Explain.

👜 **Note to Home** Students follow teacher directions for classifying pictures into groups.

Real Math • Chapter 1 • Lesson 1

LESSON 1.2 Patterns

Draw and color the missing picture.

1

2

3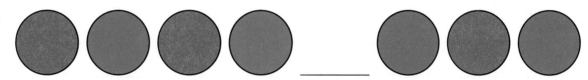

4

5

6

Note to Home Students informally define simple geometric shapes by identifying their attributes. Students then complete patterns using these simple shapes.

eTextbook This lesson is available in the *eTextbook*.

Draw and color the missing picture.

7

8

9

10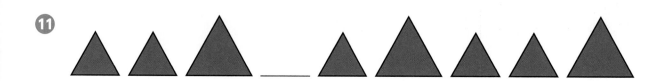

11

12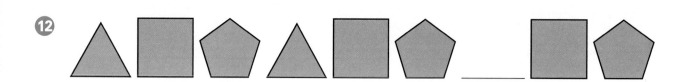

Note to Home Students informally define simple geometric shapes by identifying their attributes. Students then complete patterns using these simple shapes.

LESSON 1.3 Counting Objects

Count to find how many.

Check.

Count and check with a partner.

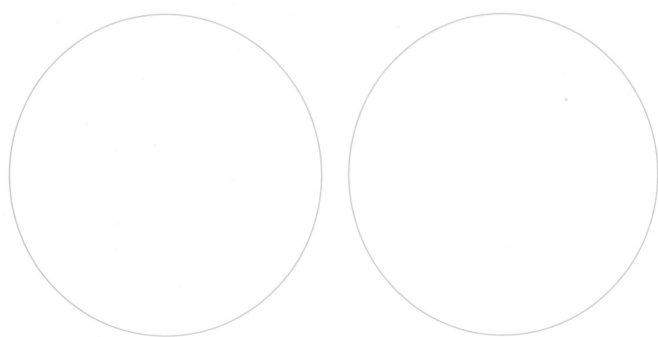

Note to Home Students practice counting from one to ten as they place counters in the circles.

Textbook This lesson is available in the *eTextbook*.

Count. Tell how many.

1

2

3

4

5 **Extended Response** There are eight triangles in this picture. Can you find all of them? Tell or show how you know.

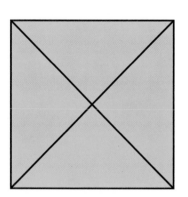

Note to Home Students count from one to ten objects.

Name _____   Date _____

How many? Mark.

1

2

3

4

5
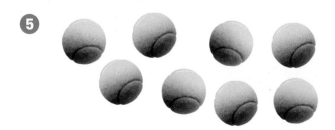

Note to Home Students count from one to ten objects. Students mark each object as it is counted so the object will be counted only once.

e Textbook This lesson is available in the *eTextbook*.

Redraw the figures so they are easy to count. The first one is done for you.

6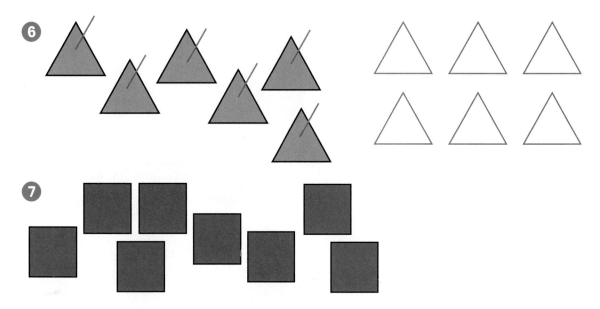

7

8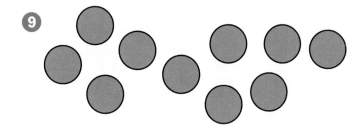

9

10 How many hearts? How many kites?

🎒 **Note to Home** Students redraw randomly arranged figures in rows to make them easier to count.

Name _____ Date _____

Counting to Share

Draw a line to separate each set into two **equal** groups.

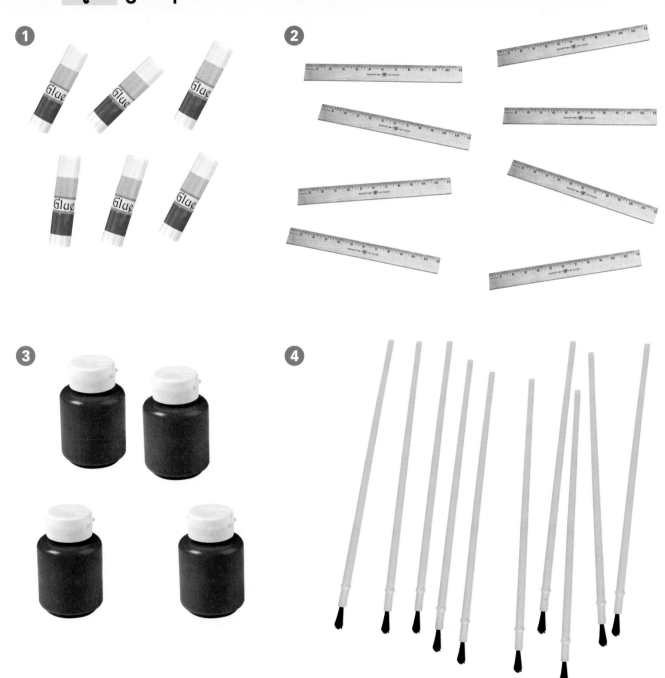

1

2

3

4

Copyright © SRA/McGraw-Hill.

🎒 **Note to Home** Students divide sets of objects into two groups of the same number of objects.

📱 **Textbook** This lesson is available in the *eTextbook.*

Listen. Follow the directions.

5

6

7

8

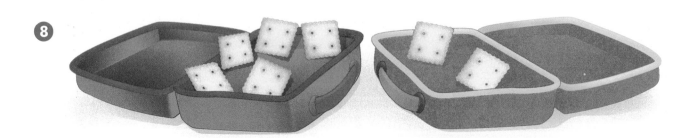

Game Play the **Which Has More? Game.**

Note to Home Students identify sets of objects as being equal, as having more, or as having fewer.

Real Math • Chapter 1 • Lesson 5

LESSON 1.6 Finger Sets

Count and show how many.

1

2

3

4

5

6

Note to Home Students form finger sets for numbers 0 to 10.

 Textbook This lesson is available in the *eTextbook*.

Count and show how many.

7

8

9

10

11

12

13 Kim is  years old.

Ann is [hand image] years old.

Who is younger? _____

Note to Home Students form finger sets for numbers 0 to 10.

Real Math • Chapter 1 • Lesson 6

Exploring 💡 Problem Solving

Name _____ Date _____

Find different ways to place three counters in the rectangle.

Show ten ways.

Do you think there are any more ways to place three counters?

Draw nine circles in every rectangle.
Show every way you find.

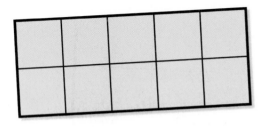
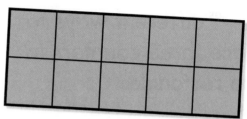

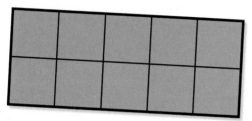
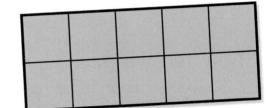

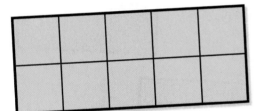
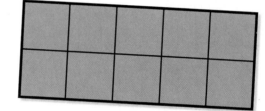

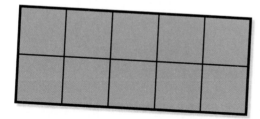
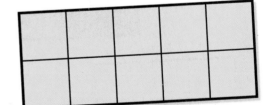

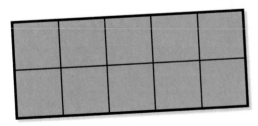
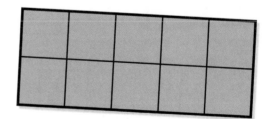

How did your pattern help you to not show
the same way two times?

How do you know there are no more ways?

Cumulative Review

Name _____ Date _____

Patterns Lesson 1.2

Draw the missing picture.

1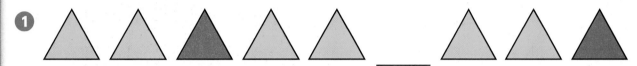

2

....

Strategies for Counting Lesson 1.4

How many? Mark.

3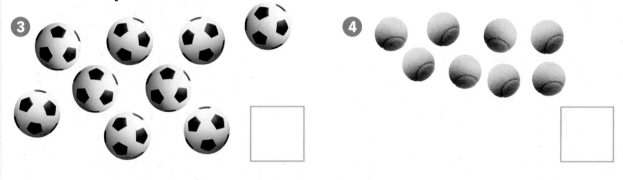

4

....

Finger Sets Lesson 1.6

Count how many and ring the correct finger set.

5

6

Cumulative Review

Strategies for Counting Lesson 1.4

Redraw the objects so they are easy to count.

7

8

Counting to Share Lesson 1.5

Draw a line to separate the set into two equal groups.

9

Counting Objects Lesson 1.3

10 There are eight triangles in this picture. Can you find all of them? Tell or show how you know.

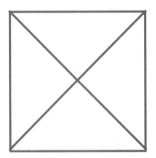

LESSON 1.7 Tracing and Writing Numbers

Count. Trace. Then copy the number.

1

2

3

4

5

6

Note to Home Students count up to ten objects and trace and copy the numbers 0 to 10.

eTextbook This lesson is available in the *eTextbook*.

Count. Trace. Then copy the number.

7

8

9

10

11

Trace the number. Then show that many hats.

12

Note to Home Students count up to ten objects and trace and copy the numbers 0 to 10.

Real Math • Chapter 1 • Lesson 7

Name _____ Date _____

Count. Trace. Then copy the number.

13

14

15

16

17

18

Note to Home Students count up to ten objects and trace and copy the numbers 0 to 10.

Count. Trace. Then copy the number.

19 4

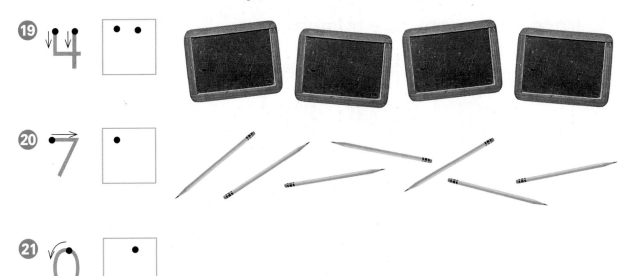

20 7

21 0

22 6

A B C X Y Z

Color the ants. Count. Write the number.

23

24

🔒 **Note to Home** Students count up to ten objects and trace and copy the numbers 0 to 10. Students practice counting objects that are partially hidden.

LESSON 1.8 Practicing Writing Numbers

Write the correct number.

1

2

3

How many geese?

4

How many pigs?

Find.   **Hide.**   **Show.**

 Note to Home Students count up to ten objects and write the number.

ⓔTextbook This lesson is available in the **eTextbook**.

Game

Tracing and Writing Numbers Game

Players: two

Materials:

- a set of **Number Cubes** (0–5 and 5–10)

- a different color of pencil or crayon for each player

HOW TO PLAY

1. Select a game: tracing with arrows, tracing without arrows, or writing.

2. Players take turns. Each turn, roll one cube. Then trace or write that number with a colored pencil. Each player uses a different color.

3. When all of the numbers in a row have been traced or written, count the numbers in each color. The player with the most numbers is the winner.

Game 1. Trace.

Game 2. Trace.

Game 3. Write.

Name _____ Date _____

Trace the correct number.

1  3 7

2  2 1

3  4 7

4  6 4

5  8 5

6 9 8

🎒 **Note to Home** Students count, choose the correct number, and trace the number.

📱 **Textbook** This lesson is available in the *eTextbook*.

Mark the corners. Count and write how many.

7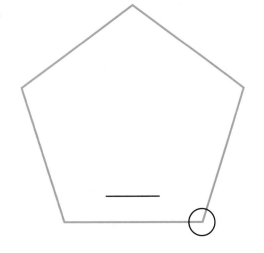

8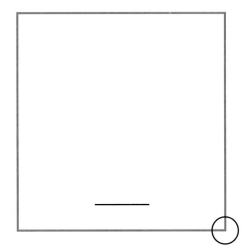

9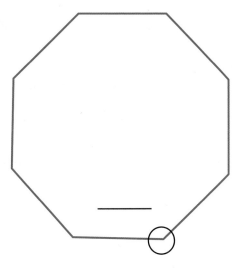

10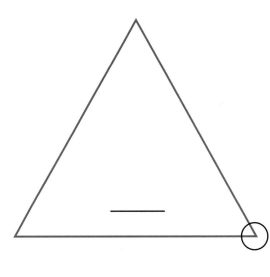

11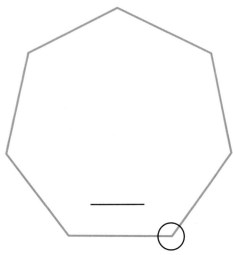

12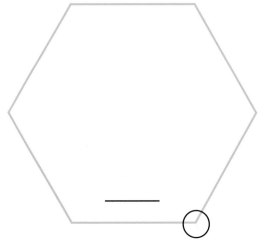

Note to Home Students count the corners of geometric figures.

Real Math • Chapter 1 • Lesson 9

Copyright © SRA/McGraw-Hill.

LESSON 1.10 Counting with the Monthly Calendar

September

Sunday	Monday	Tuesday	Wednesday	Thursday	Friday	Saturday
					1	2
3	4	5	6	7	8	9
10	11	12	13	14	15	16
17	18	19	20	21	22	23
24	25	26	27	28	29	30

September has thirty days.

Fill in the missing numbers. Then answer the questions.

1. Is September 15 a Sunday? yes   no

2. Is September 18 a Monday? yes   no

3. How many Fridays are there? _____

Note to Home Students identify days and dates on the monthly calendar and practice writing numbers.

eTextbook This lesson is available in the *eTextbook.*

27

October

Sunday	Monday	Tuesday	Wednesday	Thursday	Friday	Saturday
1	2	3	4	5	6	7
8	9	10	11	12	13	14
15	16	17	18	19	20	21
22	23	24	25	26	27	28
29	30	31				

October has thirty-one days.

Fill in the missing numbers. Then answer the questions.

4 Is October 4 a Wednesday?   yes   no

5 Is October 28 a Tuesday?   yes   no

6 How many Fridays are there? _____

7 If today is October 18, tomorrow will be October _____ .

Game Play the **Calendar Game Mat.**

 Note to Home Students identify days and dates on the monthly calendar and practice writing numbers.

LESSON 1.11 Numbers on a Clock

What time is it?

1

2

3

4

5

6

Copyright © SRA/McGraw-Hill.

Note to Home Students tell time to the hour and half hour.

eTextbook This lesson is available in the *eTextbook*.

Draw a line between the clocks that tell the same time.

7

8

9

10

11

12

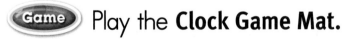 **Play the Clock Game Mat.**

Note to Home Students match times on digital and analog clocks.

Real Math • Chapter 1 • Lesson 11

Name _____ Date _____

Expanded Counting

Use your *Number Cubes*. Count and show.

1

2

3

4

5

6

Note to Home Students count ten to twenty objects and use *Number Cubes* to show the number.

e **Textbook** This lesson is available in the *eTextbook*.

31

Use your *Number Cubes.* **Count and show.**

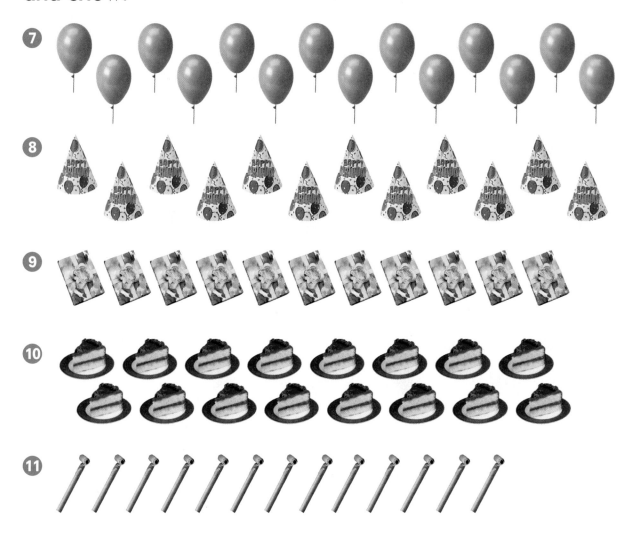

7

8

9

10

11

12 Pedro wants to draw  balloons.
How many more should Pedro draw?

Game Play the **Count to 20 by 1 or 2 Game.**

🎒 **Note to Home** Students count ten to twenty objects and use **Number Cubes** to show the number.

Real Math • Chapter 1 • Lesson 12

LESSON 1.13 Expanded Notation

Write how many.

1  ☐

2  ☐

3  ☐

4  ☐

5  ☐

6  ☐

Note to Home Students write numbers using expanded notation. When using expanded notation, the tens digit is written larger than the units digit to emphasize place value.

e Textbook This lesson is available in the *eTextbook*.

Write how many.

7

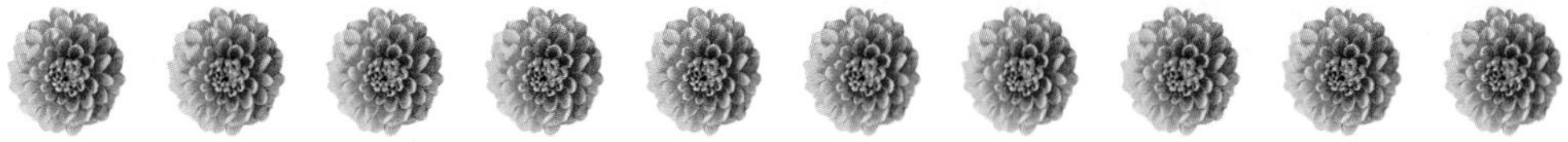

8

9

10

11

12

🔒 **Note to Home** Students write numbers using expanded notation. These numbers are read, for example, as *ten and seven.*

Name _____ Date _____

Listen to the problem.

Listen and look at how John solved the problem.

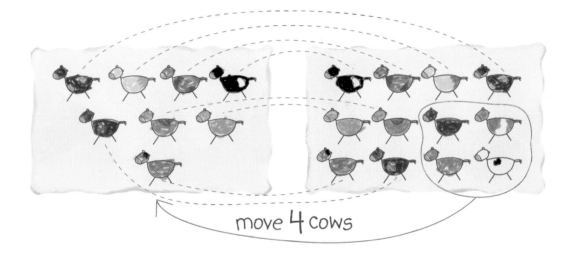

move 4 cows

What do you like about how John solved the problem?_____

What should John change? _____

Solve the problem your way.
Show how you solved it.

Cumulative Review

Name _____   Date _____

Counting with the Monthly Calendar   Lesson 1.10

Look at the calendar.

1 Fill in the missing numbers. Then answer the questions.

2 Is June 15 a Sunday? _____

3 Is June 19 a Monday?

_____

June						
SUN	MON	TUE	WED	THU	FRI	SAT
				1	2	3
4	5	6	7	8	9	10
11	12	13	14	15	16	17
18	19	20	21	22	23	24
25	26	27	28	29	30	

Practicing Writing Numbers   Lesson 1.8

Write the correct number.

4  ☐

5  ☐

Patterns   Lesson 1.2

Draw the missing picture.

6

Cumulative Review

Counting to Share Lesson 1.5

Draw a line to separate the set into two equal groups.

7

· ·

Expanded Notation Lesson 1.13

Write how many.

8

9

· ·

Reading Numbers 0–10 Lesson 1.9

Mark the corners. Count and write how many.

10 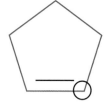 **11**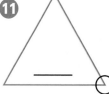

· ·

Numbers on a Clock Lesson 1.11

What time is it?

12  **13**

Name _____ Date _____

Lessons 1.6–1.9 **Count** how many and circle the correct finger set.

1

Lesson 1.2 **Draw** the missing picture.

2

3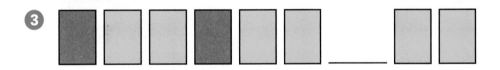

Lesson 1.4 **Redraw** the objects so they are easy to count.

4

Lesson 1.5 **Draw** a line to separate each set into two equal groups.

5

Chapter Review

Lesson 1.11 **Draw** a line between the clocks that tell the same time.

6   **3:00**

7   **12:00**

8 **7:30**

Lesson 1.13 **Write** how many.

9

 ☐

10

 ☐

Practice Test

Name _____ Date _____

Draw a line to make two equal groups.

1

2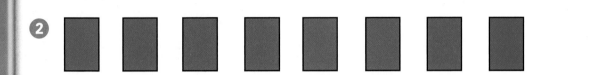

3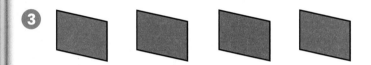

4

Write the correct number.

5

6

7

Count how many.

8

a. 4   b. 5   c. 6   d. 7

9

a. 7   b. 1   c. 9   d. 2

10

a. 7   b. 8   c. 9   d. 10

Ring the correct number.

11

a. 7   b. 9   c. 8   d. 1

12

a. 4   b. 8   c. 1   d. 0

Practice Test

Name _____ Date _____

Ring how many.

13

    a. 11   **b.** 18   **c.** 14   **d.** 13

14

    a. 20   **b.** 17   **c.** 10   **d.** 7

15

    a. 20   **b.** 10   **c.** 4   **d.** 1

Ring how many.

16

    a. 15   **b.** 16   **c.** 17   **d.** 18

17

    a. 10   **b.** 19   **c.** 1   **d.** 11

18

    a. 10   **b.** 11   **c.** 12   **d.** 13

19 **Extended Response** Draw one way to sort these objects. Explain another way.

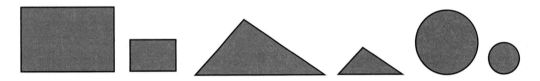

20 **Extended Response** Draw a pattern. Use every object. Tell what comes next.

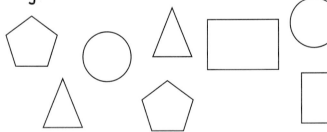

Real Math • Chapter 1

Thinking Story

How Many Piglets?

Count how many piglets. Write the number.

_____

Note to Home Students listen to the Thinking Story "How Many Piglets?" and answer questions about the story.

Textbook This lesson is available in the *eTextbook*.

Find and color the piglets. Put an X on the adult pigs.

In This Chapter You Will Learn

- about number lines.
- how to make and use graphs.

Name _____ Date _____

 What number is Fido? _____

LESSON 2.1 Number Lines

Count the objects, and write the number. Then draw a line to the correct point on the number line.

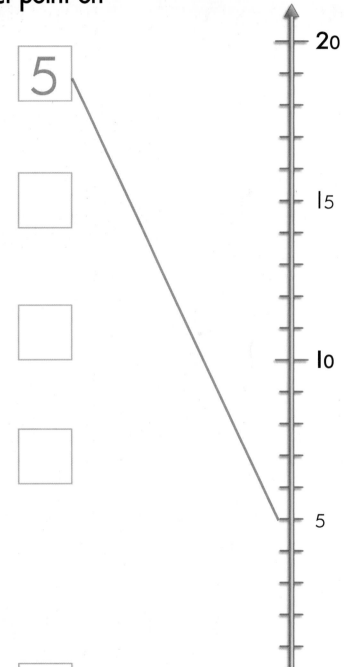

1  5

2

3

4

5

20

15

10

5

0

 Note to Home Students identify unlabeled points on a number line.

e Textbook This lesson is available in the *eTextbook*.

Write how many.

6

7    **8**

9

10

11   **12**

13

14

15

 Play the **10 Below 0 Game Mat.**

 Note to Home Students count and write numbers to twenty.

Name _____ Date _____

0 1 2 3 4 5 6 7 8 9 10 11 12 13 14 15 16 17 18 19 20

Fill in the next number.

1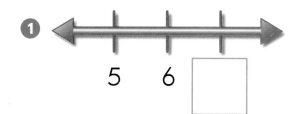

5   6   ☐

2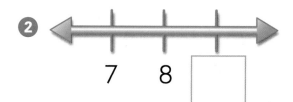

7   8   ☐

3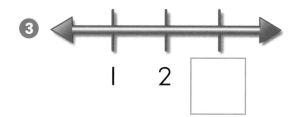

1   2   ☐

4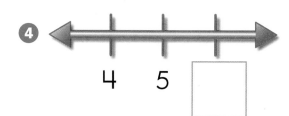

4   5   ☐

5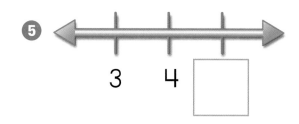

3   4   ☐

6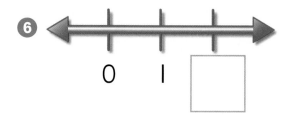

0   1   ☐

7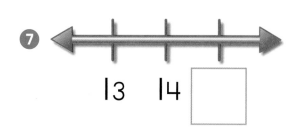

13   14   ☐

8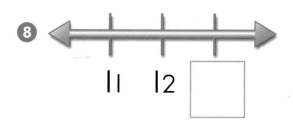

11   12   ☐

🎒 **Note to Home** Students use a number line to review number sequence.

📖 **eTextbook** This lesson is available in the *eTextbook*.

Draw one more. Then write how many.

9  _____

10 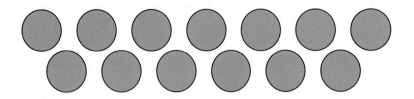 _____

11 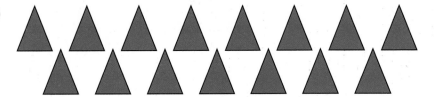 _____

12 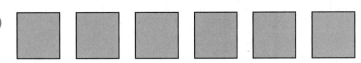 _____

13 _____

14 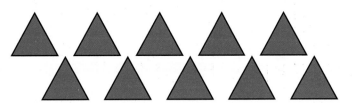 _____

15 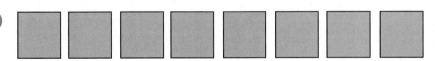 _____

16 André collects stickers. If he gets one more, he
will have 20. How many does he have now? _____

Copyright © SRA/McGraw-Hill.

🎒 **Note to Home** Students draw one more figure in each group, and then count the figures.

LESSON 2.3 What Numbers Come Before and After?

Fill in the missing numbers.

① 1 2 3 ☐ 5 6 7

② 7 ☐ 9 10 11 ☐ 13

③ 6 7 8 ☐ 10 11 12

④ 14 ☐ 16 17 18 ☐ 20

⑤ 3 4 5 6 ☐ 8 9

⑥ 2 3 4 ☐ ☐ 7 8

⑦ 13 14 15 16 ☐ 18 19

⑧ Ben is 6 years old. How old was Ben
1 year ago? _____

⑨ Ben is 6 years old. How old will Ben be
in 1 year? _____

20
19
18
17
16
15
14
13
12
11
10
9
8
7
6
5
4
3
2
1
0

 Note to Home Students use a number line to review number sequence.

eTextbook This lesson is available in the **eTextbook**.   53

Fill in the missing numbers.

10   8   ☐   10   11   12   13

11   1   2   ☐   4   ☐   6

12   7   ☐   9   10   11   ☐   13

13   15   ☐   17   18   19   20

14   10   11   12   ☐   14   15

15   ☐   3   4   5   6   7

16   ☐   6   7   8   9   ☐   11

17   9   8   7   ☐   5   4

18   ☐   19   18   17   16   15

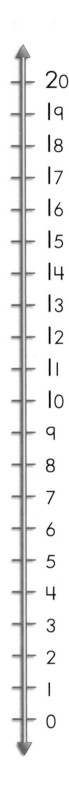

20
19
18
17
16
15
14
13
12
11
10
9
8
7
6
5
4
3
2
1
0

Note to Home Students use a number line to review number sequence.

Name _____ Date _____

Your teacher picks two counters.

Show what the graph could look like.

Red	Blue	Yellow

Red	Blue	Yellow

Red	Blue	Yellow

Red	Blue	Yellow

Red	Blue	Yellow

Red	Blue	Yellow

Did you show every possible graph?
How do you know?

Your teacher picks three counters.

Show all the possible graphs.

Red	Blue	Yellow

Red	Blue	Yellow

Red	Blue	Yellow

Red	Blue	Yellow

Red	Blue	Yellow

Red	Blue	Yellow

Red	Blue	Yellow

Red	Blue	Yellow

Red	Blue	Yellow

What pattern did you use?

How did it help you?

Cumulative Review

Name _____ Date _____

Number Lines Lesson 2.1

Count the objects, and write the number. Then draw a line to the correct point on the number line.

1 ⬜

2 ⬜

3 ⬜

0
5
10
15
20

. . . .

Finger Sets Lesson 1.6

Write how many.

4 ⬜

5 ⬜

6 ⬜

7 ⬜

Cumulative Review

Redraw the objects so they are easy to count.

8
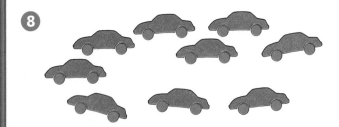

9

10

Name _____ Date _____

LESSON 2.4 Tally Marks

Use tally marks to keep count.
Then write the number.

1 How many times did your teacher

	Tallies	Total

open a book?

_____ [ ]

touch an ear?

_____ [ ]

touch the nose?

_____ [ ]

catch an eraser?

_____ [ ]

clap hands?

_____ [ ]

close the door?

_____ [ ]

point to the clock?

_____ [ ]

🎒 **Note to Home** Students use tally marks to keep accurate count of events.

Cross out one. Then write how many are left.

2 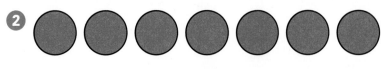 _____

3  _____

4  _____

5  _____

6 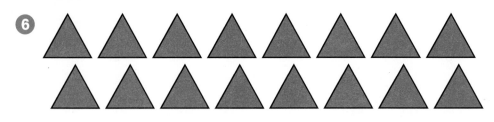 _____

7  _____

8  _____

9 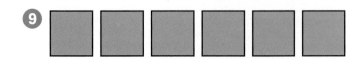 _____

10 Jamie drew 14 circles. Then she erased some.
Now there are 12 circles. How many did she erase? _____

🎒 **Note to Home** Students cross out one figure from each group, and then count the figures.

LESSON 2.5 Making Graphs

Listen to the teacher. Build your graph.

	Red	Yellow	Blue
5			
4			
3			
2			
1			

Note to Home Students create a bar-type graph to record the number of counters drawn of each color.

Textbook This lesson is available in the *eTextbook*.

Look at the picture.

1 How many 🍎 ? _____

2 How many 🍌 ? _____

3 How many 🍐 ? _____

4 Make a picture graph. Color in the correct number.

5 Are there more 🍎 or 🍌 ? Ring your answer.

👜 **Note to Home** Students collect data and record it on a picture graph.

Name _____ Date _____

Look at the **picture graph**.

How We Get to School		
	🚶	
	🚶	🚗
🚌	🚶	🚗
🚌	🚶	🚗
🚌	🚶	🚗
🚌	🚶	🚗

Number of Students 6 5 4 3 2 1

❶ How many students come by  ? _____

❷ How many students take the 🚌 ? _____

❸ How many students 🚶 ? _____

Ring the answers.

❹ Which is used by the most students?

❺ Which is used by the fewest students?

🎒 **Note to Home** Students read and interpret a picture graph.

💻 **Textbook** This lesson is available in the **eTextbook**.

Look at the picture graph.

	Our Favorite Lunch	
9	🍕	
8	🍕	
7	🍕	🌮
6	🍕	🌮
5	🍕	🌮
4	🍕	🌮
3	🥪 🍕	🌮
2	🥪 🍕	🌮
1	🥪 🍕	🌮
	sandwich pizza taco	

Number of Students

6 Ring the favorite lunch of students.

7 Ring the least favorite lunch of students.

🎒 **Note to Home** Students read and interpret a picture graph.

Name _____ Date _____

LESSON 2.7 Organizing Data

Do the coin toss activity. Use tally marks
to keep track.

	Tally Marks	Number
Heads		
Tails		

Do the activity again.

	Tally Marks	Number
Heads		
Tails		

Copyright © SRA/McGraw-Hill.

Note to Home Students explore probability and use tally marks to record the
results of a coin-toss activity.

Textbook This lesson is available in the *eTextbook*.

Alice kept count of the colors of cars that drove past her house.

Her paper looked like this.

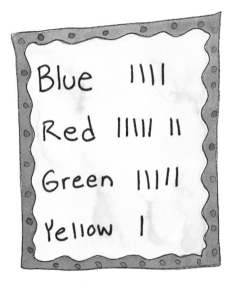

Blue   IIII

Red   IIIII II

Green   IIIII

Yellow   I

Color the graph to match Alice's count.

	Blue	Red	Green	Yellow
8				
7				
6				
5				
4				
3				
2				
1				

Note to Home Students interpret data shown by tally marks and record the data on a graph.

LESSON 2.8 Analyzing Data

Work in pairs. Roll the . Use tally marks to record **data**.

	Tallies	Totals	Class Totals
0			
1			
2			
3			
4			
5			

❶ Which number was rolled the most? _____

❷ Did every pair of students get the same results? Discuss.

🎒 **Note to Home** Students collect and record data using tally marks, while exploring probability.

Copyright © SRA/McGraw-Hill.

📖 **Textbook** This lesson is available in the *eTextbook*.

Record the data on the graph.

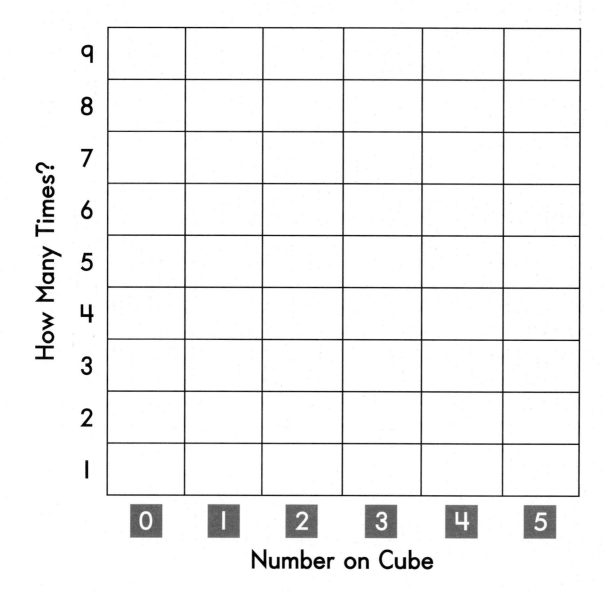

How Many Times?

9 8 7 6 5 4 3 2 1

0 1 2 3 4 5

Number on Cube

3 **Extended Response** Is the graph easier to understand than the tally marks? Discuss.

Note to Home Students transfer data, shown by tally marks on page 67, into the graph.

68   **Real Math** • Chapter 2 • Lesson 8

Name _____ Date _____

Listen to the problem.

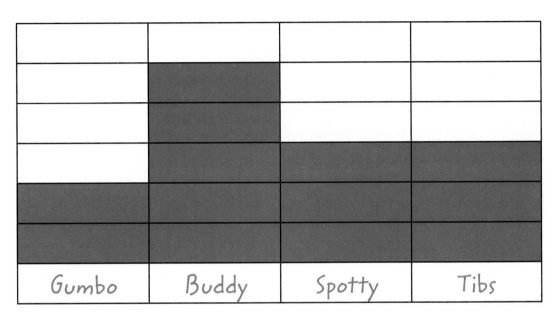

	Buddy		
	Buddy		
	Buddy	Spotty	Tibs
Gumbo	Buddy	Spotty	Tibs
Gumbo	Buddy	Spotty	Tibs
Gumbo	Buddy	Spotty	Tibs

Listen to the two ways Juan and Julia solved the problem.

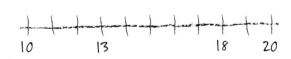

Finish Julia's solution.

Which way would you use? Why?

Mrs. Centers's class also voted on the names.
There are fifteen students in the class.

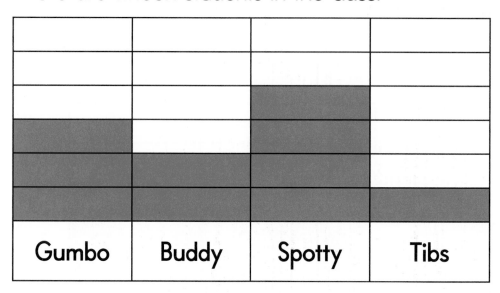

Gumbo	Buddy	Spotty	Tibs

How many students haven't voted yet? _____

Show how you solved this.

Cumulative Review

Name _____ Date _____

What Number Comes Next? Lesson 2.2

Fill in the next number.

1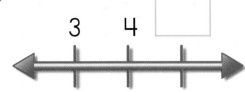

3   4   ☐

2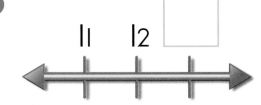

ll   l2   ☐

....

Patterns Lesson 1.2

Draw the missing figure.

3

4

....

What Numbers Come Before and After Lesson 2.3

Fill in the missing numbers.

5 7   ☐   9   l0   ll   l2

6 2   3   4   5   ☐   7   8

Cumulative Review

Tracing and Writing Numbers Lesson 1.7

7 Color the fish. Count. Write the number. _____

Making Graphs Lesson 2.5

8 How many carrots? _____

9 How many cucumbers? _____

10 How many peppers? _____

11 Make a picture graph. Color the correct number.

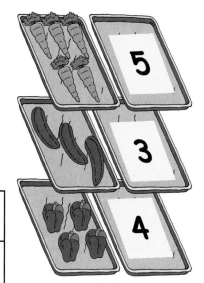

5			
4			
3			
2			
1			
	Carrots	Cucumbers	Peppers

Real Math • Chapter 2

Name _____ Date _____

Lesson 2.1 **Count** the objects and write the number. Then draw a line to the correct point on the number line.

0

5

10

15

20

①

②

Lesson 2.2 **Draw** one more. Then write how many.

③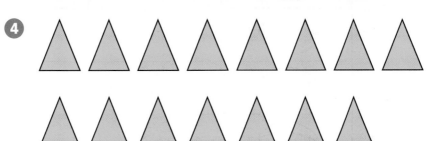

_____

④

_____

Lesson 2.5 **Look** at the picture.

5 How many baseballs? _____

6 How many basketballs? _____

7 How many footballs? _____

8 Make a picture graph. Color the correct number.

	Footballs	Basketballs	Baseballs
5	🏈	🏀	⚾
4	🏈	🏀	⚾
3	🏈	🏀	⚾
2	🏈	🏀	⚾
1	🏈	🏀	⚾

Name _____ Date _____

Write how many.

1

2

3

4

5

Write the missing numbers.

6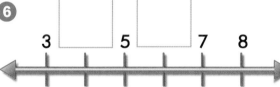

3 __ 5 __ 7 8

7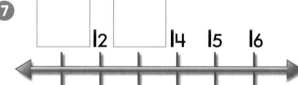

__ 12 __ 14 15 16

Write how many.

8

9

10

Count one more.

⑪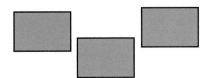

a. 5 b. 2
c. 4 d. 9

⑫

a. 2 b. 8
c. 7 d. 9

⑬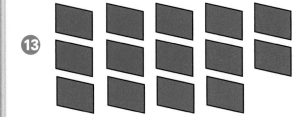

a. 5 b. 10
c. 15 d. 16

⑭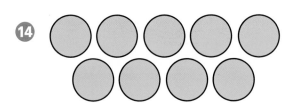

a. 1 b. 11
c. 8 d. 10

Cross out one. Count how many are left.

⑮

a. 8 b. 9 c. 7 d. 4

⑯

a. 7 b. 5 c. 9 d. 2

Name _____   Date _____

What is missing?

17

　　a. ●　　　**b.** ■　　　**c.** ★　　　**d.** ▲

18 ▲ ● ☐ ▲ __ ☐

　　a. ◯　　　**b.** ▲　　　**c.** ☐　　　**d.** ★

19

16　17　☐　19

a. 18　　**b.** 16　　**c.** 19　　**d.** 17

20

4　5　☐　7　8

a. 4　　**b.** 5　　**c.** 6　　**d.** 7

What time is it?

21
　a. 5:00
　b. 7:00
　c. 6:00
　d. 8:00

22
　a. 9:00
　b. 10:00
　c. 10:30
　d. 9:30

ⓔ Textbook This lesson is available in the *eTextbook*.

Practice Test

Extended Response **Look** at the table.

	1	2	3	4	5
Soccer ball	⚽	⚽	⚽		
Tennis ball	🎾	🎾			
Football	🏈	🏈	🏈	🏈	🏈

23 Ring the most.

24 Write how many . _____

25 Write how many . _____

26 How many more than ? _____

27 Ring the least.
Explain.

Name _____ Date _____

Thinking Story

"It's Not So Easy," Said Mr. Breezy

Count on and connect the dots.

3

18   17

19
1   16
4   2
5   15
12
8
9
6   7   10   11   13   14

What is this a picture of? _____

🎒 **Note to Home** Students listen to the Thinking Story "'It's Not So Easy,' Said Mr. Breezy" and answer questions about the story.

Put an X on the one that is different.

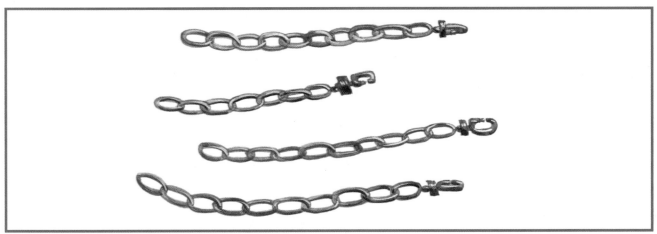

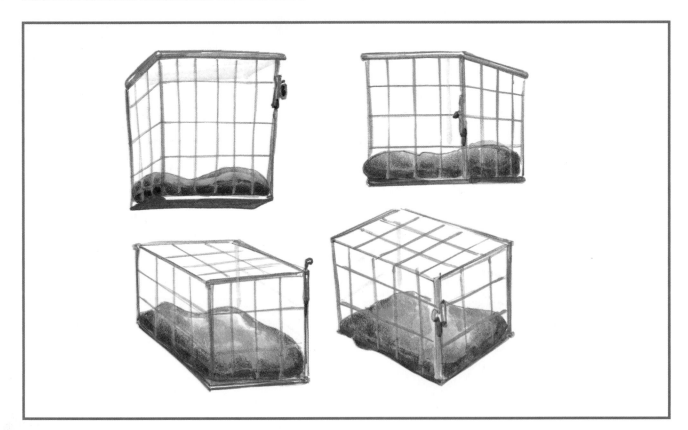

Informal Measurement

In This Chapter You Will Learn

- about *Number Strips.*
- about estimating length, weight, and capacity.
- about measuring length, weight, and capacity.

Name _____ Date _____

Listen to the problem.

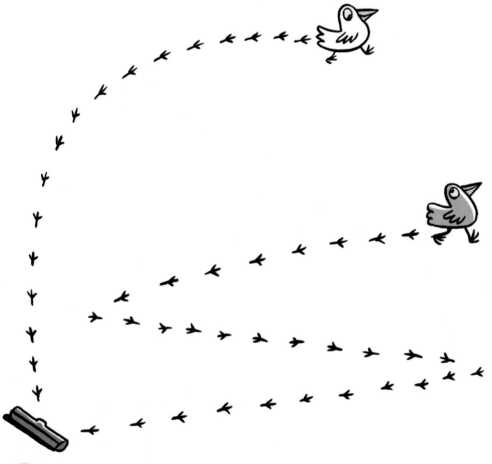

 Which bird walked more?
· ·

 Which bird is farther from the wood?
· ·

Real Math • Chapter 3

Name _____ Date _____

LESSON 3.1 Number Strips

Label each *Number Strip* with the correct number.

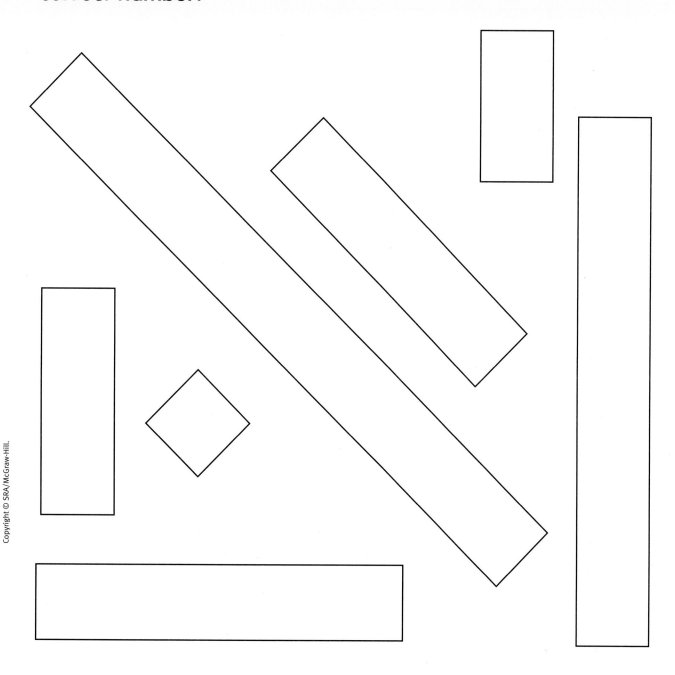

Note to Home Students identify and label **Number Strips** by length.

Textbook This lesson is available in the *eTextbook*.

Label each *Number Strip* with the correct number.

 Play the **Number Strip Game**

Note to Home Students identify and label ***Number Strips*** by length.

Real Math • Chapter 3 • Lesson 1

LESSON 3.2 **Estimating and Comparing Length I**

How long? Use your *Number Strips.*

Note to Home Students use *Number Strips* to measure.

Textbook This lesson is available in the *eTextbook.*

How long? Use your *Number Strips*.

🎒 **Note to Home** Students use *Number Strips* to measure.

Real Math • Chapter 3 • Lesson 2

LESSON 3.3 **Estimating and Comparing Length II**

Put an X on the longest side of each figure. Color the 3-sided figures blue. Color the 4-sided figures red. Color the 5-sided figures yellow.

 Note to Home Students compare the lengths of sides of geometric figures.

e Textbook This lesson is available in the *eTextbook*.

Put an X on the longest part of each zigzag. You can use paper clips to check.

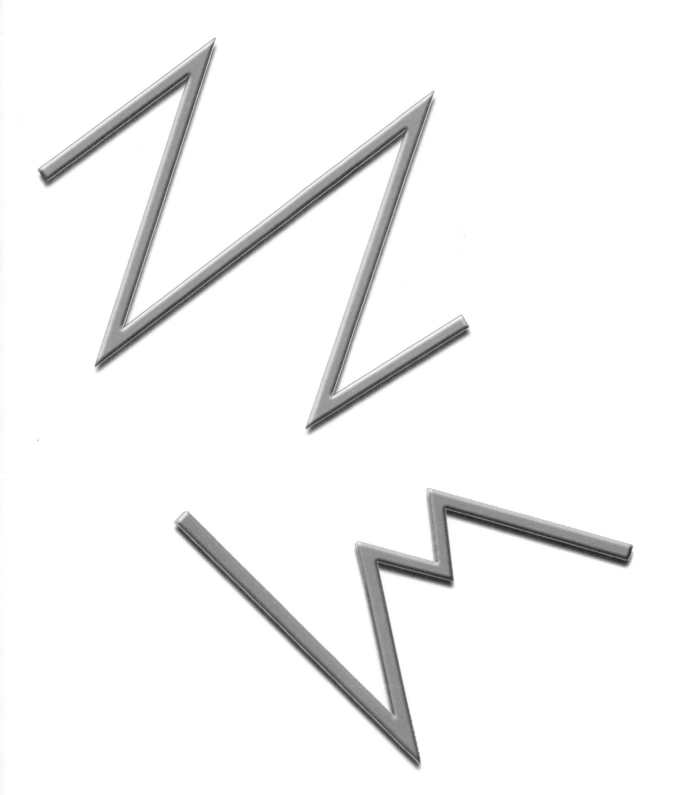

 Note to Home Students estimate the longest part.

Name _____ Date _____

Listen to the problem.

Listen to the way Evan solved the problem.

1 2 3 4 5 6 1 2 1 2 3 4 5 6 7
1 2 3 1 2 3 4 5 6 7 8 1 2 3 4

Listen to the way Emma solved the problem.

For Colin
2 and 3 and 4 and 6

For Colin's Friend
7 and 8

Copyright © SRA/McGraw-Hill.

Show how to share this snack with a friend.

Show as many ways as you can.

For Me	For My Friend

Cumulative Review

Name _____ Date _____

What Number Comes Next? Lesson 2.2

Fill in the next number.

1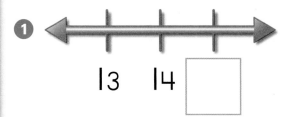

13   14   ☐

2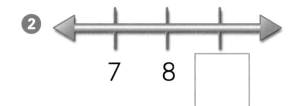

7   8   ☐

Expanded Notation Lesson 1.13

Write how many.

3    ☐

4    ☐

5    ☐

Cumulative Review

Using Graphs Lesson 2.6

	How We Get to School		
7		🚶	
6		🚶	🚗
5	🚌	🚶	🚗
4	🚌	🚶	🚗
3	🚌	🚶	🚗
2	🚌	🚶	🚗
1	🚌	🚶	🚗

Number of Students

Each picture stands for one student.

Look at the picture graph. Write the answers.

6 How many students come to school by  ? _____

7 How many students take the 🚌 ? _____

8 How many students 🚶 ? _____

Ring the answer.

9 Which is used by the fewest students?

Name _____ Date _____

Color the tallest picture red. Color the shortest picture blue. Color the other pictures any color.

 ❶
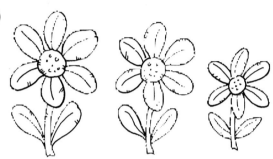

❷

❸

❹

❺

❻

🎒 **Note to Home** Students compare heights.

📱 **Textbook** This lesson is available in the **eTextbook**.

Can you find the grapes that are nearest
to the ground? Put an X on that bunch.

About how many *Number-Strip* units must
the fox walk to be under those grapes?
Use your *Number Strips* to measure.   _____

About how far from the ground are those grapes?
Use your *Number Strips* to measure.   _____

Do you think the fox can reach that high?   _____

Note to Home Students use *Number Strips* to measure.

Real Math • Chapter 3 • Lesson 4

Name _____ Date _____

Predict which object is heavier. Then use the double-pan balance to check. Draw the objects in the balance.

	Predict	Measure
1		
2		
3		

 Note to Home Students compare the weight of objects.

Textbook This lesson is available in the *eTextbook*.

Estimate the number of cubes it will take to balance. Then measure.

	Estimate	Measure
	4 about _____ ◼	**5** about _____ ◼
	6 about _____ ◼	**7** about _____ ◼
	8 about _____ ◼	**9** about _____ ◼

10 Put an X on the heaviest object.
Ring the lightest object.

 Note to Home Students estimate and measure the weight of objects.

Real Math • Chapter 3 • Lesson 5

Name _____ Date _____

Estimate how many cubes each cup will hold. Then measure.

	Estimate	Measure
	① about _____ 🔲	② about _____ 🔲
	③ about _____ 🔲	④ about _____ 🔲

Extended Response The small glass can hold about 6 cubes. How many cubes could the large glass hold? Ring your answers. Then discuss.

⑤ Is 10 cubes a good estimate?   yes   no

⑥ Is 30 cubes a good estimate?   yes   no

🔒 **Note to Home** Students estimate and measure the capacity of containers.

e Textbook This lesson is available in the *eTextbook*.

Ring the container that holds more.

🎒 **Note to Home** Students compare capacity.

Name _____ Date _____

Listen to the problem.
Match the object with the paper that tells
how long it is.

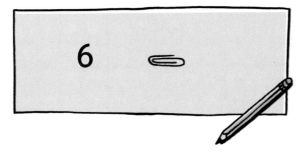

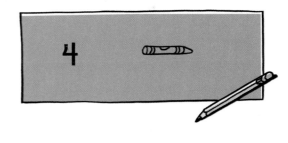

Did everyone get the same answer? _____

Can different answers be correct? _____

Draw three other objects you could use to measure.

```
┌─────────────────────────────────────────┐
│                                         │
│                                         │
│                                         │
│                                         │
└─────────────────────────────────────────┘
```

```
┌─────────────────────────────────────────┐
│                                         │
│                                         │
│                                         │
│                                         │
└─────────────────────────────────────────┘
```

```
┌─────────────────────────────────────────┐
│                                         │
│                                         │
│                                         │
│                                         │
└─────────────────────────────────────────┘
```

Cumulative Review

Name _____ Date _____

Count the objects and write the number. Then draw a line to the correct point on the number line.

1

2

3

20

15

10

5

0

Counting to Share Lesson 1.5

Draw a line to separate each into two equal groups.

4

5

Measuring Height Lesson 3.4

Color the tallest object red. Color the shortest object blue. Choose any color for the other objects.

6    **7**    **8**

Number Strips Lesson 3.1

Label each Number Strip with the correct number.

10

11

12

13

14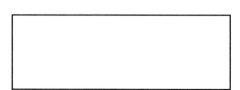

Name _____ Date _____

Lesson 3.1 **Label** each *Number Strip* with the correct number.

①

②

Lessons 3.2–3.3 **③** Draw a ring around the shortest object.

④ Place an X on the longest object.

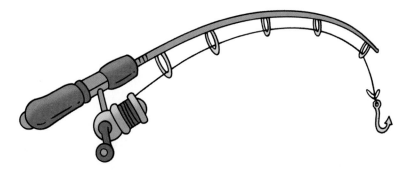

Lesson 3.4 **Ring** the tallest object. Put an X on the shortest object.

5

6

Lesson 3.5 **Draw** the objects on the correct sides of the balance.

7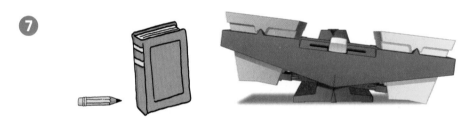

Lesson 3.6 **Ring** the pool that holds more.

8

Practice Test

Name _____ Date _____

How long? Use your Number Strips.

1  _____

2  _____

3  _____

Put an X on the longest side.

4

5

6

Which group is equal to the first one?

7

a.   b.

c.   d.

8

a.

b.

c.

d.

9

a.   b.   c.   d.

Ring the missing number.

10

4   5   ▢

a. 6   b. 5
c. 7   d. 9

11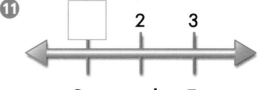

▢   2   3

a. 2   b. 5
c. 1   d. 0

Name _____ Date _____

Measure the height.

12 Ring the tallest.

 a.  b.  c.  d.

13 Ring the tallest.

a.   b.    c.   d.

14 Ring the shortest.

a.   b.   c.  d.

15 Ring the shortest.

a.  b.   c.   d.

Extended Response **Estimate.**

16 Draw the and to show the result.

17 Ring what is in the other tray.

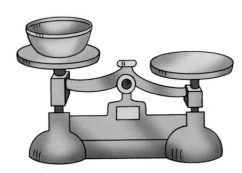

Look at the pictures.

18 Ring the box that holds more.

19 Draw a box that holds more.

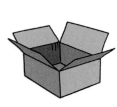  

Name _____ Date _____

Thinking Story

Willy in the Water

Find a path back to the beach towel, and collect five shells along the way.

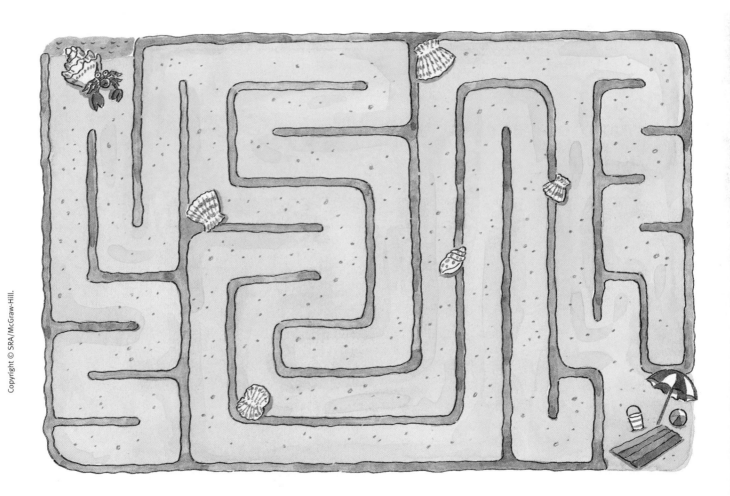

Note to Home Students listen to the Thinking Story "Willy in the Water" and answer questions about the story.

eTextbook This lesson is available in the *eTextbook*.

How many buckets tall is the sand castle? ____

How many bottles of sunblock tall is the sea lion? ____

CHAPTER 4
Informal Addition and Subtraction

In This Chapter You Will Learn

- how to use finger sets for addition.
- different ways to write addition and subtraction problems.
- how to use a number line for addition and subtraction.
- how to use *Number Strips* for addition and subtraction.

Problem Solving

Name _____   Date _____

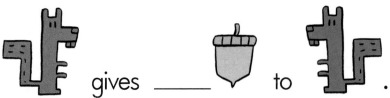

gives _____ 🌰 to 🦎 .

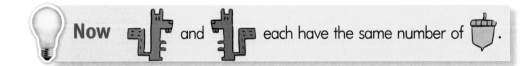

💡 **Now** 🦎 and 🦎 each have the same number of 🌰 .

Copyright © SRA/McGraw-Hill.

Name _____ Date _____

Use finger sets to add.

1.

2.

3.

4.  ☐

5.

6.

7.

8.

Copyright © SRA/McGraw-Hill.

🎒 **Note to Home** Students display finger sets to calculate the sum of two addends, represented by groups of small objects.

📖 **Textbook** This lesson is available in the *eTextbook*.

113

Use finger sets to add.

9 | 2 | ☐

10 | 3 | ☐

11 | 5 | ☐

12 | 5 | ☐

13 | 5 | ☐

14 | 6 | ☐

15 | 8 | ☐

16 | 5 | ☐

Game Play the **Hidden Counters Game** (Adding).

🎒 **Note to Home** Students display finger sets to calculate the sum of two addends, one represented by groups of small objects, and the other represented by a number so that the answer cannot be counted directly.

LESSON 4.2 Adding with Hidden Counters

How many in all?

1  ▢

2  ▢

3  ▢

4  ▢

5    ▢

Note to Home Students solve addition exercises with counters, some of which are hidden. When solving hidden-counter exercises, students must calculate the sums rather than simply counting the total number of counters.

e Textbook This lesson is available in the *eTextbook*.

How many in all?

Note to Home Students solve addition exercises with counters, some of which are hidden. When solving hidden-counter exercises, students must calculate the sums rather than simply counting the total number of counters.

Name _____ Date _____

How many in all?
Do you see a pattern?

Copyright © SRA/McGraw-Hill.

🎒 **Note to Home** Students practice addition with hidden counters to discover the order law.

📱 **Textbook** This lesson is available in the *eTextbook*.

117

The number tells how many fish are behind the rock. Write how many fish there are in all.

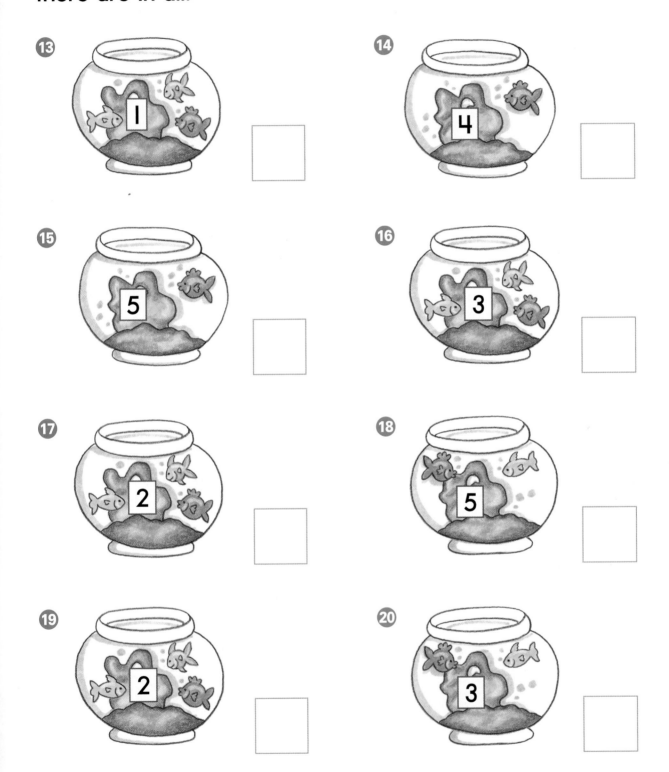

13

14

15

16

17

18

19

20

🔒 **Note to Home** Students practice addition with hidden objects.

LESSON 4.4 Using Finger Sets to Subtract

How many now?

1

2

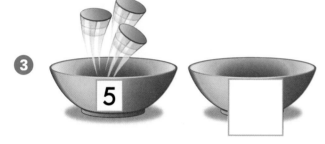

3

4

5

6

7

8

Note to Home Students solve subtraction exercises with counters, some of which are hidden.

eTextbook This lesson is available in the *eTextbook*.

How many now?

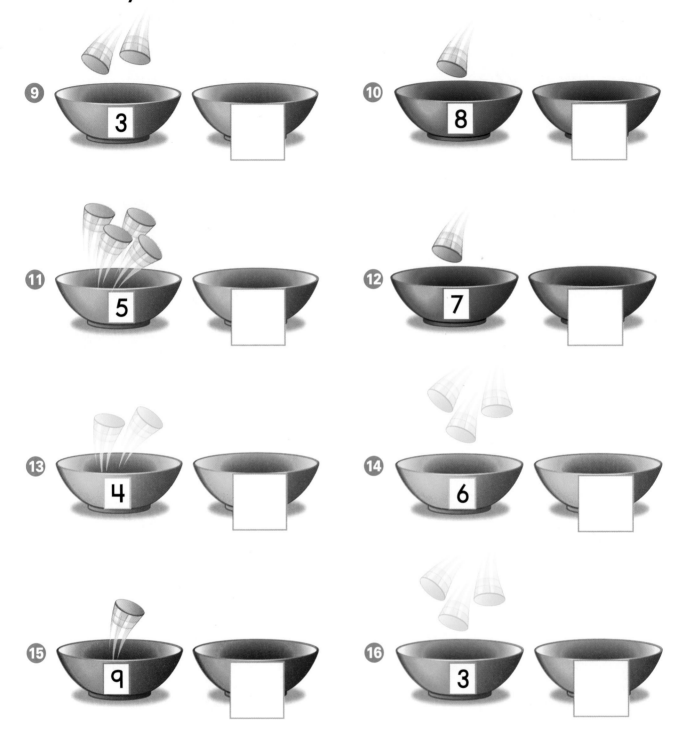

 Game Play the **Don't Take Them All Game.**

🎒 **Note to Home** Students solve addition and subtraction exercises with hidden counters.

Real Math • Chapter 4 • Lesson 4

LESSON 4.5 Adding and Subtracting (Horizontal Form)

How many now?

1

$2 + 3 = $ _____

2

$3 - 1 = $ _____

3

$3 - 2 = $ _____

4

$1 + 2 = $ _____

5

$3 + 3 = $ _____

6

$2 - 1 = $ _____

Note to Home Students solve concrete addition and subtraction exercises in which one number is hidden. Students are also introduced to the matching number sentence.

Textbook This lesson is available in the *eTextbook*.

How many now?

 7

$2 + 2 =$ ____

 8

$2 - 1 =$ ____

 9

$2 + 1 =$ ____

 10

$3 - 1 =$ ____

 **11**

$3 - 3 =$ ____

 12

$0 + 0 =$ ____

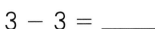 **Game** Play the **Hidden Counters Game** (Subtracting).

 Note to Home Students solve concrete addition and subtraction exercises in which one number is hidden. Students are also exposed to the matching number sentence.

Name _____ Date _____

What pattern do you see? _____

_____

What color is 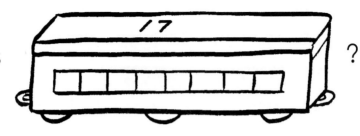 ?

Jordon will use counters.

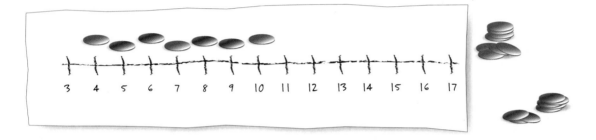

Hannah will write numbers.

Show how you solved the problem.

Cumulative Review

Name _____ Date _____

What Number Comes Next? Lesson 2.2

Fill in the next number.

1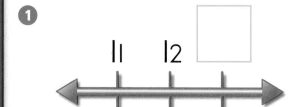

11 12 [ ]

2 4 5 [ ]

Estimating and Comparing Length I Lesson 3.2

How long? Use your *Number Strips*.

3 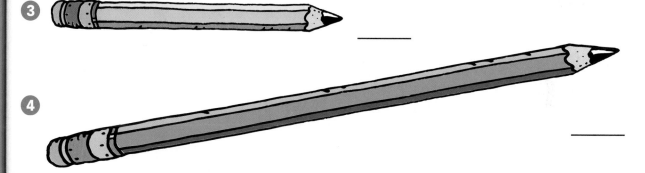 _____

4 _____

Numbers on a Clock Lesson 1.11

Fill in the clock.

5

6

7

6:00   1:30   11:30

Cumulative Review

Using Finger Sets to Add Lesson 4.1

Use finger sets to add.

What Number Comes Next? Lesson 2.2

Draw one more. Then write how many.

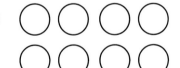

 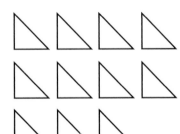

LESSON 4.6 Adding and Subtracting with Fingers Out of Sight

How many now?

1

2

3

4

5

6

7

8

 Note to Home Students solve concrete addition and subtraction exercises with one number hidden. Students use finger sets to solve the exercises, as in previous lessons, but now do so without looking at their fingers.

e Textbook This lesson is available in the **eTextbook**.

127

Listen to the problems. Discuss.

⑨ Rayyan had 6 marbles. Then he bought 3 more. Now how many marbles does Rayyan have? _____

⑩ Nadine had 6 marbles. She lost 2 of them. Now how many marbles does Nadine have? _____

⑪ Rayyan had 6 marbles. Then he bought 3 sports cards. Now how many marbles does Rayyan have? _____

⑫ **Extended Response** There are 3 students wearing sneakers. There are 4 students wearing sweaters. Among this group, 2 of the students are boys. What is the fewest number of students there could be? Explain your answer. _____

 Note to Home Students solve word problems.

Real Math • Chapter 4 • Lesson 6

Name _____ Date _____

Adding and Subtracting (Vertical Form)

Solve these exercises.

Watch the signs.

1
```
   8
 + 2
```

2
```
   6
 − 1
```

3
```
   1
 + 3
```

4
```
   3
 + 1
```

5
```
   0
 + 8
```

6
```
   6
 − 0
```

7
```
   2
 + 4
```

8
```
   7
 − 2
```

9 7 + 2 = _____

10 7 − 1 = _____

11 7 + 0 = _____

12 9 − 2 = _____

13 6 + 2 = _____

14 6 + 1 = _____

15 4 − 0 = _____

16 4 − 1 = _____

17 9 − 0 = _____

18 9 − 1 = _____

Note to Home Students solve addition and subtraction exercises.

eTextbook This lesson is available in the *eTextbook*.

Listen to the problems. Discuss.

19 Andrea has 5 red pencils and 2 blue pencils. How many pencils does she have?

_____

20 Michael has 5 pencils and 2 pens. How many pencils does he have? _____

21 Erin had 5 pencils. Then she gave 2 of them to Keith. Now how many pencils does she have? _____

22 Raulito had 5 pencils. He gave 1 to Brett and 1 to Julia. Now how many does he have? _____

23 A total of 6 students went to the fair. Sneakers were worn by 3 students. Hats were worn by 4 students. Two of the students were girls.
How many students were boys? _____
How many students did not wear hats? _____
How many students wore sweaters? _____

Game Play the **Duck Pond Game.**

🎒 **Note to Home** Students solve word problems.

Name _____ Date _____

Use the number line.

5 6 7 8 9 10

1 Start at 5. Count on 1, and then ring the number you land on.

5 6 7 8 9 10

2 Start at 6. Count on 2, and then ring the number you land on.

5 6 7 8 9 10

3 Start at 7. Count on 2, and then ring the number you land on.

5 6 7 8 9 10

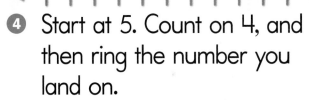

4 Start at 5. Count on 4, and then ring the number you land on.

5 6 7 8 9 10

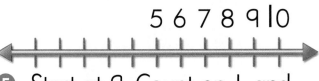

5 Start at 9. Count on 1, and then ring the number you land on.

5 6 7 8 9 10

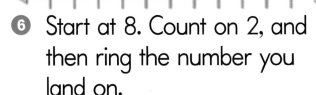

6 Start at 8. Count on 2, and then ring the number you land on.

🎒 **Note to Home** Students practice moving on a number line in preparation for using a number line to add and subtract.

📖 **Textbook** This lesson is available in the *eTextbook*.

Listen to the problems and discuss.

7 Henry walks 3 blocks to school. How many blocks does he walk to and from school?

_____

8 Arjun walked 5 blocks to the park. Then he walked 2 more blocks to the library. How many blocks did he walk? _____

9 **Extended Response** Janet lives 6 blocks from the library and 1 block from school. How far is the library from school? Discuss your answer.

Note to Home Students solve word problems.

Copyright © SRA/McGraw-Hill.

LESSON 4.9 Adding and Subtracting on a Number Line

Solve these exercises. Use the number line.

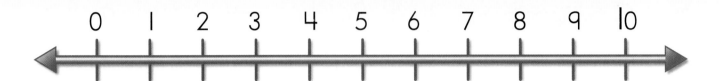

0   1   2   3   4   5   6   7   8   9   10

1 $4 + 2 = $ _____

2 $7 + 1 = $ _____

3 $5 - 1 = $ _____

4 $8 - 3 = $ _____

5 $3 + 2 = $ _____

6 $3 + 3 = $ _____

7 $2 + 3 = $ _____

8 $6 - 3 = $ _____

9 $8 - 2 = $ _____

10 $9 - 2 = $ _____

1   2   3   4   5   6   7   8

🎒 **Note to Home** Students solve addition and subtraction exercises using the number line.

📖 **Textbook** This lesson is available in the *eTextbook*.

Solve these exercises. Use the number line.

⑪ $3 - 1 =$ _____

⑫ $1 + 2 =$ _____

⑬ $7 + 2 =$ _____

⑭ $6 - 1 =$ _____

⑮ $6 + 2 =$ _____

⑯ $8 + 1 =$ _____

⑰ $1 + 3 =$ _____

⑱ $6 - 2 =$ _____

⑲ $5 + 2 =$ _____

⑳ $5 + 1 =$ _____

㉑ $8 - 2 =$ _____

㉒ $4 - 0 =$ _____

㉓ $8 - 3 =$ _____

㉔ $4 + 0 =$ _____

㉕ $5 - 3 =$ _____

 **Note to Home** Students solve addition and subtraction exercises using the number line.

Real Math • Chapter 4 • Lesson 9

LESSON 4.10 Adding with Number Strips

Fill in the correct numbers on the
Number Strips.

2	
4	

| 1 | |
| 3 | |

| 5 | |
| 3 | |

| 2 | |
| 2 | |

| 3 | |
| 3 | |

| 2 | |
| 3 | |

Copyright © SRA/McGraw-Hill.

Note to Home Students use *Number Strips* to solve addition exercises.

eTextbook This lesson is available in the *eTextbook.*

Fill in the correct numbers on the *Number Strips.*

3	
5	

4	
4	

6	
4	

2	
3	

4	
5	

1	
4	

Note to Home Students use *Number Strips* to solve addition exercises.

Real Math • Chapter 4 • Lesson 10

LESSON 4.11 Subtracting with Number Strips

Fill in the correct numbers on the
Number Strips.

5	3

7	3

4	2

7	4

5	2

6	3

🎒 **Note to Home** Students use *Number Strips* to solve subtraction exercises.

📺 **Textbook** This lesson is available in the *eTextbook.*

Fill in the correct numbers on the *Number Strips.*

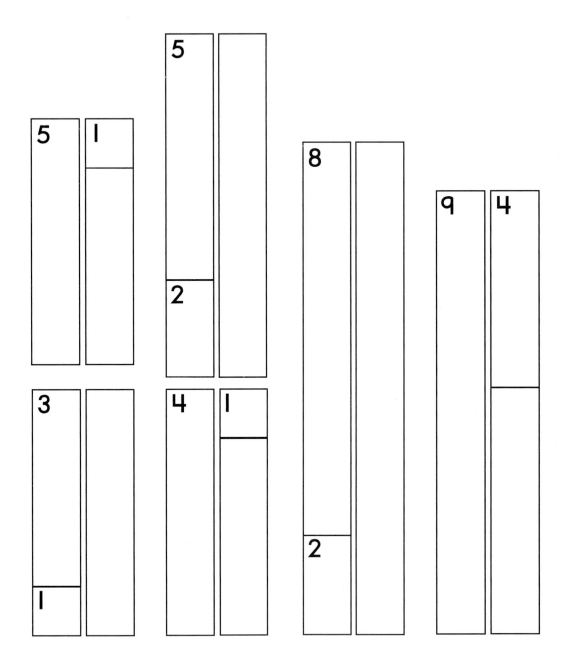

Note to Home Students use *Number Strips* to solve addition and subtraction exercises.

138   Real Math • Chapter 4 • Lesson 11

Name _____ Date _____

Listen to the teacher.

The monkey can go ← and → → or

_____ or _____ .

Listen to the problem.

Show how the 🐒 can go.

Show two different ways. ☐ ☐

Show three more ways.

How many ways did your class show? _____

Cumulative Review

Name _____ Date _____

Counting with the Monthly Calendar Lesson 1.10

Look at the calendar.
Answer the questions.

1 Is September 21 a

Sunday? _____

2 How many Thursdays

are there? _____

		September				
SUN	MON	TUE	WED	THU	FRI	SAT
					1	2
3	4	5	6	7	8	9
10	11	12	13	14	15	16
17	18	19	20	21	22	23
24	25	26	27	28	29	30

- -

What Numbers Come Before and After? Lesson 2.3

Fill in the missing numbers.

3 16   17   18   ☐   20

4 7   ☐   9   10   11   ☐   13   14

- -

Tally Marks Lesson 2.4

Cross out one. Then write how many are left.

5 ■ ■ ■ ■ ■ ■   ☐

6 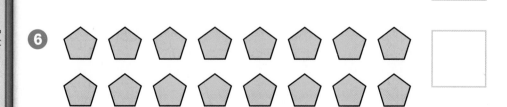   ☐

Cumulative Review

Adding with Hidden Counters Lesson 4.2

How many in all?

  □

  □

  8 □

Patterns Lesson 1.2

Draw the missing picture.

     ___

      ___

Measuring Height Lesson 3.4

Ring the tallest picture.

Name _____ Date _____

Lesson 4.1 Use finger sets to add.

1

2

Lesson 4.3 The number tells how many fish are behind the rock. Write how many fish there are in all.

3  2

4  5

Lessons 4.4–4.5 How many now?

5 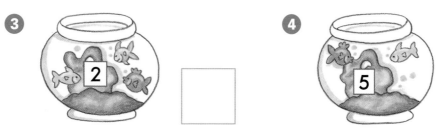 8

8 − 3 = ____

6 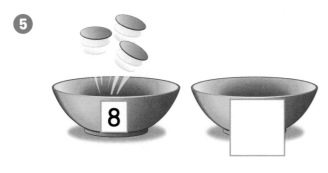 10

10 − 3 = ____

Lesson 4.6 **Listen.** Write the answer on the line.

7 Rayyan had 6 tennis balls. He lost 2 of them. Now how many tennis balls does Rayyan have? _____

8 Nadine had 8 baseballs. Then she bought 2 tennis balls. Now how many baseballs does Nadine have? _____

Lesson 4.7 **Solve** these problems. Watch the signs.

9   8   **10**   6   **11** 4 − 0 = _____
    + 2   − 3

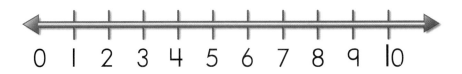

0 1 2 3 4 5 6 7 8 9 10

Lessons 4.8–4.9 **Solve** these problems. Use the number line.

12 7 + 2 = _____   **13** 9 − 2 = _____

14 2 + 4 = _____   **15** 3 + 7 = _____

16 9 − 3 = _____

Practice Test

Name _____ Date _____

How many in all?

1  _____

2  _____

3  _____

4  _____

Solve. Use the number line.

5 Start on 7. Hop on 2. Ring the number.

6 Start on 9. Hop on 7. Ring the number.

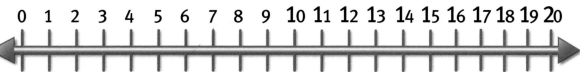

e Textbook This lesson is available in the *eTextbook*.

What time is it?

7    **a.** 12:00   **b.** 1:00   **c.** 2:00   **d.** 3:00

8    **a.** 12:30   **b.** 1:00   **c.** 12:00   **d.** 2:30

9    **a.** 9:00   **b.** 6:00   **c.** 6:30   **d.** 7:00

Estimate.

10 Which one is the tallest?

 **a.**    **b.**   **c.**    **d.**

11 Which one is the shortest?

 **a.**    **b.**   **c.**   **d.**

Name _____ Date _____

Add or subtract. Use the number line.

12 3 + 5 = ____
    a. 7   **b.** 5
    c. 9   **d.** 8

13 8 + 1 = ____
    a. 3   **b.** 8
    c. 9   **d.** 5

14 9 − 2 = ____
    a. 13   **b.** 7
    c. 9   **d.** 4

15 10 − 3 = ____
    a. 7   **b.** 3
    c. 4   **d.** 1

Add or subtract. Use the number line.

16
    6
  + 3
  □
    a. 8   **b.** 9
    c. 3   **d.** 6

17
    8
  − 2
  □
    a. 3   **b.** 14
    c. 7   **d.** 6

18
    5
  + 3
  □
    a. 11   **b.** 13
    c. 8   **d.** 4

19
    5
  − 0
  □
    a. 8   **b.** 5
    c. 2   **d.** 6

Number line: 10, 9, 8, 7, 6, 5, 4, 3, 2, 1, 0

Add and subtract using *Number Strips.*

20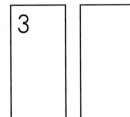

21

22 Extended Response How are the exercises above alike and different?

_____

_____

23 Extended Response Draw 3 pairs of number strips that add up to 10.

10

Name _____   Date _____

Manolita's
AMAZING
NUMBER MACHINE

Find the number words in the word find.

n	r	t	o	v	e	x	n	t	v
t	w	o	n	e	o	n	e	x	i
e	a	n	s	i	x	f	s	k	o
n	t	n	v	g	o	o	e	s	t
s	o	v	o	h	e	u	v	t	o
t	s	t	e	t	h	r	e	e	n
i	n	i	n	e	g	c	n	f	h
e	e	t	g	x	u	e	f	i	v
t	e	n	h	x	t	e	o	v	h
u	b	e	g	i	h	c	n	e	t

one
two
three
four
five
six
seven
eight
nine
ten

Note to Home Students listen to the Thinking Story "Manolita's Amazing Number Machine" and answer questions about the story.

eTextbook This lesson is available in the *eTextbook*.

149

Color the Amazing Number Machine.

Look at the symbols on the machine.
What do you think it does?

_____

_____

Introducing Addition and Subtraction Facts

In This Chapter You Will Learn
- more about addition and subtraction.
- about coins and bills.

Name _____ Date _____

Listen to the problem.

8¢ 5¢ 6¢ 9¢ 4¢ 2¢ 3¢ 7¢ 1¢

You have 10

 What two things can you buy?

 Show as many answers as you can.

_____

_____

_____

Name _____ Date _____

How many cents?

1 _____ ¢

2 _____ ¢

3 _____ ¢

4 _____ ¢

5 _____ ¢

6 _____ ¢

🎒 Note to Home Students add with pennies and nickels.

📱 **eTextbook** This lesson is available in the *eTextbook*.

Draw coins to make the correct amount. Use nickels whenever you can. You may use play coins to help.

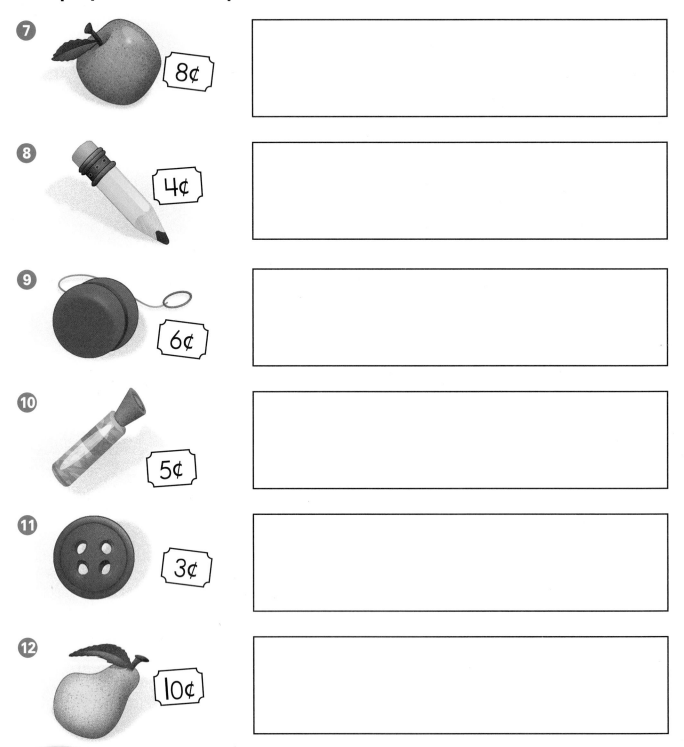

7 8¢

8 4¢

9 6¢

10 5¢

11 3¢

12 10¢

Game Play the **Pennies and Nickels Game.**

Note to Home Students use pennies and nickels to form given amounts of money.

Real Math • Chapter 5 • Lesson 1

Name _____   Date _____

$1 and $5 Bills

How much money?

1    $ _____

2  $ _____

3   $ _____

4

 $ _____

5  $ _____

 Note to Home Students add with $1 and $5 bills.

eTextbook This lesson is available in the *eTextbook.*

Draw bills to make the correct amount.
Use as few bills as possible.

 6

7

8

9

10

 Play the **$1 and $5 Bills Game.**

Note to Home Students form given amounts of money with $1 and $5 bills.

Real Math • Chapter 5 • Lesson 2

LESSON 5.3 Sums of 10

Connect sets of 2 bags so there are
10 marbles in each set.

Copyright © SRA/McGraw-Hill.

Note to Home Students connect pairs of addends that make sums of ten.

Draw a *Number Strip* to make 10. The first one is done for you. Check using your strips.

4	5	7	3	8

🎒 **Note to Home** Students combine two *Number Strips* that equal the length of the 10-strip.

158   **Real Math** • Chapter 5 • Lesson 3

LESSON 5.4 Adding 5

Write the number sentences.

1 $5 +$ ☐ $=$ ____

2 $5 +$ ☐ $=$ ____

3 ☐ $+$ ☐ $=$ ____

4 ☐ $+$ ☐ $=$ ____

5 ☐ $+$ ☐ $=$ ____

Note to Home Students use finger sets to do addition exercises with 5 as one of the addends. By raising the finger set for 5 on one hand and the finger set for the other addend on the other hand, and then putting them together, students obtain the finger set representing the sum.

e Textbook This lesson is available in the *eTextbook*.

Add. Use finger sets if you need to.

6   3 + 2 + 4 = _____

7   2 + 3 + 3 = _____

8   1 + 4 + 5 = _____

9   4 + 3 + 1 = _____

10   4 + 3 + 2 = _____

11 3 + 2 + 4 + 1 = _____

12 Troy had 15 lemons. He squeezed
5 lemons to make lemonade. He sold
all the lemonade. Then he squeezed
5 more lemons. How many lemons has
Troy used? _____

🎒 **Note to Home** Students find addends that make 5, and then add a third number.

Name _____ Date _____

Add. Use statue addition.

1  + 2 = _____

2  + 1 = _____

3 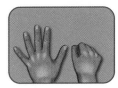 + 1 = _____

4 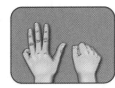 + 2 = _____

5  + 3 = _____

6 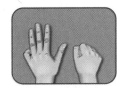 + 3 = _____

7  + 2 = _____

8  + 2 = _____

9  + 3 = _____

10  + 3 = _____

Note to Home Students do these exercises using statue addition, a form of finger-set addition in which a finger set is raised for only one of the addends and students must imagine raising fingers for the other addend.

ⓔTextbook This lesson is available in the *eTextbook*.

Listen and discuss.

11 Todd's table has 3 legs. Shannon's table has 4 legs. Whose table is taller?

12 In 3 years Daniel will be 9 years old. How old is he now?

13 Rebecca had 5 books. She read one of them 4 times and one of them 3 times. Now how many books does Rebecca have?

14 Michelle is 7 years old. How old will she be in 3 years?

15 **Extended Response** Marlo is 5 years old. Emma is 2 years older than Marlo. Juanita is younger than Emma but older than Marlo. None of the children are the same age. How old is Juanita? Tell how you know.

Note to Home Students solve word problems.

Name _____ Date _____

Subtract. Use statue subtraction.

1 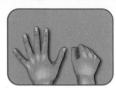 − 2 = _____

2  − 3 = _____

3  − 1 = _____

4 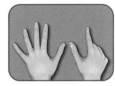 − 3 = _____

5  − 3 = _____

6  − 2 = _____

7  − 4 = _____

8  − 4 = _____

9  − 2 = _____

10  − 3 = _____

Copyright © SRA/McGraw-Hill.

Note to Home Students do these exercises using statue subtraction, a form of finger-set subtraction in which students do not actually turn down fingers for the number being subtracted; they only think about what the resulting finger set would look like.

Textbook This lesson is available in the **eTextbook**.

163

Find the answer. You can use statue subtraction to help.

If you have this much money	and you buy this	you will have this much left
11 $5	basketball $3	
12 $1 $1 $1 $1	train $2	
13 $5 $1	car $4	
14 $5 $5	monkey $5	
15 $5 $1	top $1	

🎒 **Note to Home** Students solve subtraction problems involving money.

Name _____ Date _____

Listen to the problem.

Phil has these blocks:

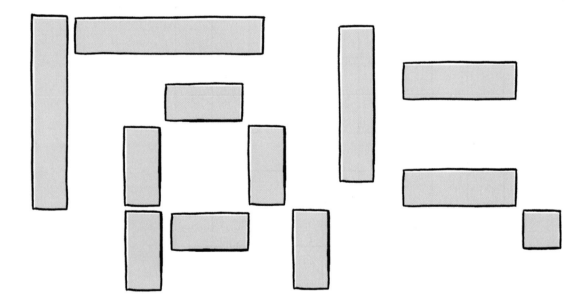

How can Phil use the blocks
to spell his name?

Draw your answer on the back.

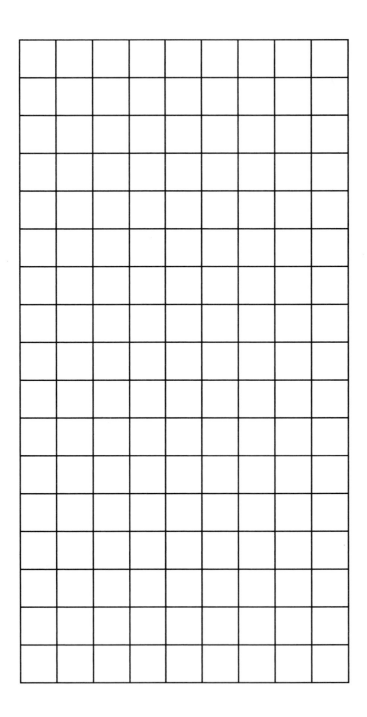

Cumulative Review

Name _____ Date _____

Reading Numbers 0 to 10 Lesson 1.9

Mark the corners. Count and write how many.

1

2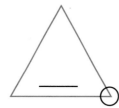

What Number Comes Next? Lesson 2.2

Draw one more. Then write how many.

3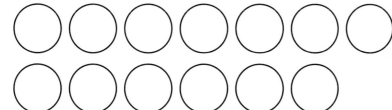

4

Adding and Subtracting Lesson 4.7

Add or subtract.

5 $\begin{array}{r} 6 \\ +\,4 \\ \hline \end{array}$

6 $\begin{array}{r} 9 \\ -\,2 \\ \hline \end{array}$

7 $\begin{array}{r} 3 \\ +\,2 \\ \hline \end{array}$

8 $\begin{array}{r} 4 \\ -\,0 \\ \hline \end{array}$

Cumulative Review

Estimating and Measuring Capacity **Lesson 3.6**

Ring the container that holds more.

9

10

Adding and Subtracting (Horizontal Form) **Lesson 4.5**

How many?

11

$1 + 2 = \underline{\hspace{2cm}}$

12

$2 + 3 = \underline{\hspace{2cm}}$

Pennies and Nickels **Lesson 5.1**

How many cents?

13   _____ ¢

14   _____ ¢

LESSON 5.7 Mental Addition

Do these in your head. Then write the answers.

① $\begin{array}{r} 5 \\ +1 \\ \hline \end{array}$ ② $\begin{array}{r} 2 \\ +1 \\ \hline \end{array}$ ③ $\begin{array}{r} 5 \\ +2 \\ \hline \end{array}$ ④ $\begin{array}{r} 6 \\ +0 \\ \hline \end{array}$

⑤ $8 + 1 = $ _____   ⑥ $4 + 2 = $ _____

⑦ $5 + 2 = $ _____   ⑧ $4 + 1 = $ _____

⑨ $2 + 2 = $ _____   ⑩ $1 + 2 = $ _____

⑪ $3 + 2 = $ _____   ⑫ $3 + 1 = $ _____

⑬ $8 + 2 = $ _____   ⑭ $7 + 2 = $ _____

Garage SALE!

Note to Home Students do addition exercises mentally.

Textbook This lesson is available in the *eTextbook*.

Is there enough money? Write yes or no.
Discuss how you knew.

If you have this much money	Can you buy these things?	yes or no?
15 $5	🍽️ $3 🧸 $4	
16 $5 $1	🍽️ $3 🍽️ $3	
17 $5 $1 $1	🚚 $4 🚛 $4	
18 $5 $1	🍽️ $3 🌸 $2	
19 $1 $1 $1 $1	🌸 $2 🌸 $2	

 Note to Home Students solve problems by comparing sums of money and sums of prices.

Name _____ Date _____

LESSON 5.8 Mental Subtraction

Do these in your head. Then write the answers.

1 7 − 3 = _____   **2** 7 − 1 = _____

3 4 − 1 = _____   **4** 4 − 2 = _____

5 5 − 3 = _____   **6** 3 − 3 = _____

7   9   **8**   9   **9**   8   **10**   7
    − 1   − 0   − 3   − 2

11   6   **12**   8   **13**   7   **14**   5
     − 2   − 2   − 0   − 2

🎒 **Note to Home** Students do subtraction exercises mentally.

e **Textbook** This lesson is available in the *eTextbook.*

Do these in your head. Then write the answers.

⑮ 7 + 2 = _____　　　　⑯ 6 − 0 = _____

⑰ 4 − 3 = _____　　　　⑱ 5 − 1 = _____

⑲ 2 + 2 = _____　　　　⑳ 2 + 4 = _____

㉑　　7　　　㉒　　4　　　㉓　　8　　　㉔　　6
　　+ 3　　　　　− 0　　　　　+ 1　　　　　− 3

㉕　　6　　　㉖　　6　　　㉗　　1　　　㉘　　5
　　+ 3　　　　　− 1　　　　　− 0　　　　　+ 3

🎒 **Note to Home** Students do addition and subtraction exercises mentally.

Name _____ Date _____

Function Machines I

Find the rule.

1

in →	out
5	3
6	4
7	5
8	6
9	7

The rule is _____

2

in →	out
7	8
6	7
3	4
2	3
1	2

The rule is _____

3

in →	out
8	7
7	6
5	4
3	2
1	0

The rule is _____

4

in →	out
5	5
4	4
3	3
6	6
7	7

The rule is _____

5

in →	out
3	6
4	7
2	5
6	9
7	10

The rule is _____

Note to Home Students solve addition and subtraction function problems.

e Textbook This lesson is available in the *eTextbook*.

Find the output and the rule.

6

in	out
1	2
4	5
6	7
3	

The rule is _____

7

in	out
4	6
3	5
2	
0	2

The rule is _____

8

in	out
6	4
7	5
3	
2	0

The rule is _____

9

in	out
5	4
7	
8	7
3	2

The rule is _____

10

in	out
0	3
5	8
2	
4	7

The rule is _____

11

in	out
7	4
6	
5	2
4	1

The rule is _____

Note to Home Students solve addition and subtraction function problems.

Real Math • Chapter 5 • Lesson 9

Find the rule.

1

in → out	
4	2
8	6
2	0
5	3

The rule is _____

2

in → out	
1	1
9	9
5	5
7	7

The rule is _____

3

in → out	
7	10
2	5
5	8
1	4

The rule is _____

4

in → out	
2	3
8	9
5	6
7	8

The rule is _____

Note to Home Students solve addition and subtraction function problems.

Find the output and the rule.

5

in	out
3	5
6	8
7	9
1	

The rule is _____

6

in	out
7	10
5	8
1	
0	3

The rule is _____

7

in	out
5	2
8	
6	3
4	1

The rule is _____

Find the input and the rule.

8

in	out
6	4
	2
3	1
10	8

The rule is _____

9

in	out
10	7
5	2
	4
6	3

The rule is _____

10

in	out
4	6
2	4
1	3
	10

The rule is _____

🎒 **Note to Home** Students solve addition and subtraction function problems.

LESSON 5.11 Function Machines III

Find the input or output and the rule.

1

in	out
4	6
1	3
	8
8	10

The rule is _____

2

in	out
1	0
8	7
5	
3	2

The rule is _____

3

in	out
1	1
6	
2	2
	9

The rule is _____

4

in	out
10	7
5	2
3	0
4	

The rule is _____

5

in	out
5	10
2	4
1	2
4	

The rule is _____

🎒 **Note to Home** Students solve function problems.

📱 **Textbook** This lesson is available in the *eTextbook*.

Find the input or output and the rule.

6

in	out
10	5
2	1
	4
4	2

The rule is _____

7

in	out
6	9
5	
2	5
	4

The rule is _____

8

in	out
4	2
	5
10	8
3	1

The rule is _____

9

in	out
3	6
	4
5	10
1	2

The rule is _____

10

in	out
8	9
1	2
2	
5	6

The rule is _____

 Note to Home Students solve function problems.

Exploring Problem Solving

Name _____ Date _____

How can Jane make a +5 machine?

_____

How can Jane make a +6 machine?

_____

Cumulative Review

Name _____ Date _____

Estimating and Comparing Length I Lesson 3.2

How long? Use your Number Strips.

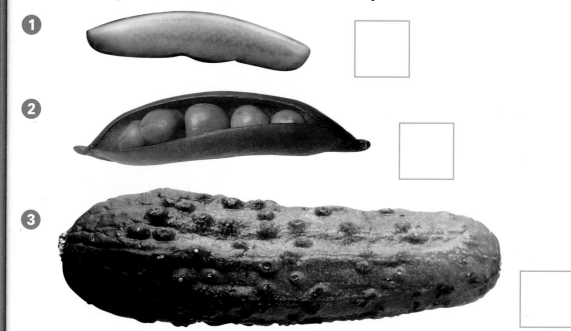

1. ☐

2. ☐

3. ☐

Using Finger Sets to Subtract Lesson 4.4

How many?

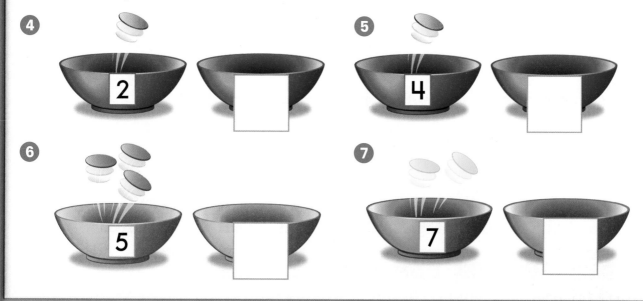

4. 2 | ☐

5. 4 | ☐

6. 5 | ☐

7. 7 | ☐

Cumulative Review

$1 and $5 Bills Lesson 5.2

How much money?

     $ _____

 $ _____

  $ _____

Patterns Lesson 1.2

Draw the missing picture.

11  _____

12   _____

Tally Marks Lesson 2.4

Cross out one. Then write how many are left.

13

14

Name _____ Date _____

Lessons 5.1–5.2 **How much money?**

1   _____ ¢

2   _____ ¢

3   _____ ¢

4   $ _____

5    $ _____

Lesson 5.3 **Connect 2 bags so there are 10 marbles.**

6

7

8

Lesson 5.5 **Add.** Use statue addition.

9 $+ 2 =$ _____

10 $+ 3 =$ _____

11 $+ 1 =$ _____

Lesson 5.6 **Subtract.** Use statue subtraction.

12 $- 1 =$ _____

13 $- 2 =$ _____

14 $- 1 =$ _____

Lessons 5.7–5.8 **Do** these in your head. Then write the answers.

15 $5 + 2 =$ _____   **16** $9 - 3 =$ _____

17 $6 - 1 =$ _____   **18** $9 + 2 =$ _____

19 $4 + 2 =$ _____   **20** $8 - 3 =$ _____

Practice Test

Name _____ Date _____

How much money?

1   _____ ¢

2   _____ ¢

3    $ _____

4   $ _____

Draw and name a *Number Strip* to make 10.

5 | 7 |

6 | I |

Solve. Use the number line.

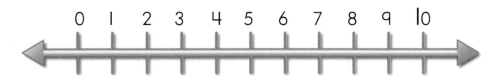

7. Start on 5. Hop on 3.
   a. 6   **b.** 2   **c.** 9   **d.** 8

8. Start on 1. Hop on 6.
   a. 7   **b.** 6   **c.** 8   **d.** 2

9. Start on 8. Hop on 2.
   a. 4   **b.** 6   **c.** 10   **d.** 9

Solve.

10. Kade has 5 pencils. He gave away 2 pencils. How many pencils does he have now?
    a. 5   **b.** 3   **c.** 7   **d.** 6

11. Nick has 7 erasers. He gets 2 more erasers. How many erasers does he have now?
    a. 5   **b.** 7   **c.** 6   **d.** 9

12. Tabatha has 6 markers. She gives away half of them. How many markers does she have now?
    a. 3   **b.** 6   **c** 4   **d.** 5

Name _____ Date _____

Ring the missing number.

13 $7 + \underline{\quad} = 9$

   a. 1   **b.** 3   **c.** 2   **d.** 9

14 $2 + \underline{\quad} = 6$

   a. 4   **b.** 6   **c.** 2   **d.** 3

15 $8 - \underline{\quad} = 2$

   a. 6   **b.** 8   **c.** 2   **d.** 5

16 $10 - \underline{\quad} = 5$

   a. 3   **b.** 5   **c.** 10   **d.** 7

Do these in your head. Ring the answer.

17
$$\begin{array}{r} 1 \\ + 5 \\ \hline \square \end{array}$$

  a. 5   **b.** 4
  c. 7   **d.** 6

18
$$\begin{array}{r} 9 \\ - 3 \\ \hline \square \end{array}$$

  a. 7   **b.** 6
  c. 5   **d.** 9

19
$$\begin{array}{r} 3 \\ + 3 \\ \hline \square \end{array}$$

  a. 3   **b.** 7
  c. 6   **d.** 5

20
$$\begin{array}{r} 6 \\ - 4 \\ \hline \square \end{array}$$

  a. 3   **b.** 2
  c. 1   **d.** 4

Extended Response **Make** your own outputs and rule.

Find the rule.

㉑

in	out
2	
3	
4	
5	

The rule is _____

㉒

in	out
0	4
2	6
4	8
6	10

The rule is _____

Extended Response **Find** the mistake in each function machine. Correct it and explain why it was wrong.

㉓

in	out
5	7
1	3
4	6
3	6

The rule is +2 _____

㉔

in	out
9	4
6	1
8	4
7	2

The rule is −5 _____

㉕

in	out
3	5
5	7
7	9
2	4

The rule is −2 _____

Name _____ Date _____

Design a sign for a lemonade stand.

Note to Home Students listen to the Thinking Story "The Lemonade War" and answer questions about the story.

eTextbook This lesson is available in the *eTextbook*.

How many glasses of lemonade will Marcus need if everyone in line wants to buy one glass? _____

CHAPTER 6 More Addition Facts

In This Chapter You Will Learn
- more about addition and subtraction.
- about coins and bills.

Name _____ Date _____

Listen to the problem.

1 6¢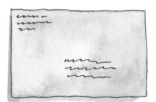

2 13¢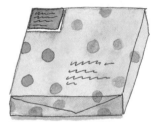

3 11¢

4 5¢

5 15¢

6 18¢

LESSON 6.1 The Addition Table

	1	**2**	**3**	**4**	**5**
1	A	B	C	D	E
2	B	F	G	H	I
3	C	G	J	K	L
4	D	H	K	M	N
5	E	I	L	N	O

Figure out these code words.

1 ____ ____ ____
1, 2   1, 5   5, 1

2 ____ ____ ____ ____
4, 4   1, 1   4, 1   5, 1

3 ____ ____
2, 4   1, 5

4 ____ ____ ____ ____
4, 2   2, 5   1, 4   1, 5

5 ____ ____ ____
1, 1   2, 5   4, 4

6 ____ ____ ____ ____
1, 2   5, 5   5, 4   5, 1

7 ____ ____ ____
5, 5   5, 3   1, 4

8 ____ ____ ____ ____
4, 4   1, 5   1, 1   5, 4

Note to Home Students complete a puzzle to help prepare them to use an addition table.

eTextbook This lesson is available in the *eTextbook*.

Play the Addition Table Game.

+	0	1	2	3	4	5
0	0	1	2	3	4	5
1	1	2	3	4	5	6
2	2	3	4	5	6	7
3	3	4	5	6	7	8
4	4	5	6	7	8	9
5	5	6	7	8	9	10

Now use the Addition Table to do these exercises:

9 $3 + 5 =$ _____

10 $3 + 4 =$ _____

11 $0 + 4 =$ _____

12 $4 + 5 =$ _____

13 $2 + 5 =$ _____

14 $5 + 2 =$ _____

Note to Home Students use the Addition Table to find sums to 10.

LESSON 6.2 Adding Doubles 0–5

The coats on the Button people have the same number of buttons in back as they do in front.

How many buttons are there on each coat? Write a number sentence to show. The first one is done for you.

1 __2__ + __2__ = __4__

2 _____ + _____ = _____

3 _____ + _____ = _____

4 _____ + _____ = _____

5 _____ + _____ = _____

6 _____ + _____ = _____

Note to Home Students count visible buttons and then double the number to find the doubles sum.

e Textbook This lesson is available in the *eTextbook.*

Addition Practice

Roll a Double Game

Players:
Two or more

Materials:

- Two 0–5 *Number Cubes*

- 20 counters or pennies

HOW TO PLAY

- Place 20 counters in a pile.

- Take turns rolling both cubes.

- If a double is rolled, say the sum.

- If correct, take a counter from the pile.

- Keep taking turns.

- The player with the most counters at the end of the game is the winner.

I played the game with _____ .

Name _____ Date _____

LESSON 6.3 Adding 10 and Adding 9

Do the easier exercise first. Then it will help you do the harder one.

Easier Exercises

① $7 + 10 =$ ____

③ $5 + 5 =$ ____

⑤ $7 + 7 =$ ____

⑦ $10 + 4 =$ ____

⑨ $6 + 6 =$ ____

⑪ $8 + 2 =$ ____

⑬ $10 + 6 =$ ____

Harder Exercises

② $7 + 9 =$ ____

④ $5 + 6 =$ ____

⑥ $8 + 7 =$ ____

⑧ $9 + 4 =$ ____

⑩ $6 + 7 =$ ____

⑫ $7 + 2 =$ ____

⑭ $9 + 6 =$ ____

⑮ **Extended Response** Complete the patterns. Discuss.

10	11	12	13			16			19
9+1	9+2			9+5			9+8		9+10

🎒 **Note to Home** Students find the sums for the $+9$ and $+10$ facts and notice relationships between them.

e Textbook This lesson is available in the **eTextbook**.   197

Copyright © SRA/McGraw-Hill.

Play the Addition Table Game.

+	5	6	7	8	9	10
0	5	6	7	8	9	10
1	6	7	8	9	10	11
2	7	8	9	10	11	12
3	8	9	10	11	12	13
4	9	10	11	12	13	14
5	10	11	12	13	14	15

Now use the Addition Table to do these exercises:

16 4 + 10 = _____

17 4 + 9 = _____

18 6 + 10 = _____

19 6 + 9 = _____

20 3 + 9 = _____

21 3 + 10 = _____

Note to Home Students use the Addition Table to find the sums for +9 and +10 facts.

LESSON 6.4 Addition Facts—Sums to 20

What numbers are missing on some of these strips? Write them in.

1
| 6 | | 9 | |
| | 10 | | |

2
| 5 | | 7 | |
| | 10 | | |

3
| 7 | | 8 | |
| | 10 | | |

4
| 4 | | 8 | |
| | 10 | | |

5
| 7 | | 9 | |
| | 10 | | |

6
| 6 | | 7 | |
| | 10 | | |

🎒 **Note to Home** Students use **Number Strips** to practice addition facts.

📱 **Textbook** This lesson is available in the **eTextbook**.

Play the Addition Table Game.

+	5	6	7	8	9	10
5	10	11	12	13	14	15
6	11	12	13	14	15	16
7	12	13	14	15	16	17
8	13	14	15	16	17	18
9	14	15	16	17	18	19
10	15	16	17	18	19	20

Now use the Addition Table to do these exercises:

7 $6 + 5 =$ _____

8 $4 + 9 =$ _____

9 $5 + 7 =$ _____

10 $5 + 8 =$ _____

11 $2 + 9 =$ _____

12 $4 + 10 =$ _____

Note to Home Students use the Addition Table to find sums in the 10–20 range.

Name _____   Date _____

LESSON 6.5 **Adding Doubles 6–10**

The coats on the Button Twins have the same number of buttons in back as they do in front.

How many buttons does each pair of twins have on their coats? Write a number sentence to show. The first one is done for you.

SOCIAL STUDIES ① __6__ + __6__ = __12__

② ___ + ___ = ___   ③ ___ + ___ = ___

④ 5 + 5 = ___   ⑤ 6 + 6 = ___   ⑥ 7 + 7 = ___

⑦ 8 + 8 = ___   ⑧ 9 + 9 = ___   ⑨ 10 + 10 = ___

⑩ 2 + 2 = ___   ⑪ 4 + 4 = ___   ⑫ 3 + 3 = ___

⑬ 1 + 1 = ___   ⑭ 0 + 0 = ___

 Note to Home Students practice doubles sums.

Textbook This lesson is available in the *eTextbook*.

Copyright © SRA/McGraw-Hill.

+	0	1	2	3	4	5
0	0	1	2	3	4	5
1	1	2	3	4	5	6
2	2	3	4	5	6	7
3	3	4	5	6	7	8
4	4	5	6	7	8	9
5	5	6	7	8	9	10

+	5	6	7	8	9	10
5	10	11	12	13	14	15
6	11	12	13	14	15	16
7	12	13	14	15	16	17
8	13	14	15	16	17	18
9	14	15	16	17	18	19
10	15	16	17	18	19	20

15 Study the Addition Tables. Then color the doubles sums.

16 **Extended Response** What patterns do you see in the tables? _____

_____

Game Play the **Harder Roll a Double Game.**

Note to Home Students notice patterns in the Addition Table.

Name _____ Date _____

Progress on the Addition Table

**Find each sum.
You can use the
Addition Table.**

+	0	1	2	3	4	5	6	7	8	9	10
0	0	1	2	3	4	5	6	7	8	9	10
1	1	2	3	4	5	6	7	8	9	10	11
2	2	3	4	5	6	7	8	9	10	11	12
3	3	4	5	6	7	8	9	10	11	12	13
4	4	5	6	7	8	9	10	11	12	13	14
5	5	6	7	8	9	10	11	12	13	14	15
6	6	7	8	9	10	11	12	13	14	15	16
7	7	8	9	10	11	12	13	14	15	16	17
8	8	9	10	11	12	13	14	15	16	17	18
9	9	10	11	12	13	14	15	16	17	18	19
10	10	11	12	13	14	15	16	17	18	19	20

1
$$\begin{array}{r} 10 \\ +\ 1 \\ \hline \end{array}$$

2
$$\begin{array}{r} 2 \\ +\ 5 \\ \hline \end{array}$$

3
$$\begin{array}{r} 7 \\ +\ 7 \\ \hline \end{array}$$

4
$$\begin{array}{r} 9 \\ +\ 5 \\ \hline \end{array}$$

5
$$\begin{array}{r} 0 \\ +\ 10 \\ \hline \end{array}$$

6
$$\begin{array}{r} 1 \\ +\ 8 \\ \hline \end{array}$$

7 6 + 6 = _____

8 6 + 7 = _____

9 6 + 8 = _____

10 6 + 9 = _____

11 9 + 1 = _____

12 0 + 6 = _____

13 8 + 2 = _____

14 4 + 4 = _____

15 9 + 9 = _____

Note to Home Students review sums using the Addition Table.

Textbook This lesson is available in the *eTextbook*.

Listen. Then solve.

16 There are 2 cars that have a flat tire. How many tires are not flat? _____

17 Sarah ate 3 apples. Alan ate 2 apples. How many apples were there to start?

_____

18 Petra planted 10 radish seeds in her garden. There were 8 sprouts. How many did not sprout? _____

19 There are 2 cows in the barn. How many cows are there altogether? _____

Note to Home Students solve word problems.

Name _____ Date _____

Abby has $2.

She saves $3 each week.

When can she buy the horn?

Ryan is making a table to solve the problem.

Emily is acting out the problem with play money.

Show how you solved the problem.

Abby can buy the horn in _____ weeks.

Cumulative Review

Name _____ Date _____

Making Graphs Lesson 2.5

Fruit in Basket

1 How many apples? _____

2 How many bananas? _____

- -

Adding and Subtracting with Fingers Out of Sight Lesson 4.6

Listen to the problems. Write the answer.

3 Rayyan had 5 marbles. Then he bought 2 more. Now how many marbles does Rayyan have? _____

4 Nadine had 6 marbles. She lost 2 of them. Now how many marbles does Nadine have? _____

- -

Mental Addition Lesson 5.7

Do these in your head. Then write the answers.

5 $\begin{array}{r} 4 \\ +1 \\ \hline \end{array}$ **6** $\begin{array}{r} 3 \\ +1 \\ \hline \end{array}$ **7** $\begin{array}{r} 5 \\ +2 \\ \hline \end{array}$ **8** $\begin{array}{r} 6 \\ +0 \\ \hline \end{array}$

- -

Adding with Hidden Counters Lesson 4.2

How many in all?

9

10

Cumulative Review

Adding Doubles 0–5 Lesson 6.2

The coats on the Button people have the same number of buttons in back as they do in front.

How many buttons are there on each coat? Write a number sentence to show.

⑪

⑫

_____ + _____ = _____   _____ + _____ = _____

Numbers on a Clock Lesson 1.11

What time is it?

⑬

⑭

Name _____ Date _____

Draw coins to make 20¢.
Try to do it with:

1 2 coins

2 3 coins

3 4 coins

4 7 coins

5 8 coins

🔖 **Note to Home** Students use combinations of pennies, nickels, and dimes to form 20¢ from a specified number of coins.

ⓔ **Textbook** This lesson is available in the *eTextbook*.

Use coins to figure out how much each pair would cost.

Write your answer on the line.

6 _____¢   7¢   5¢

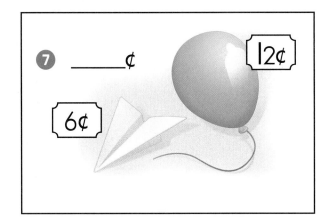

7 _____¢   12¢   6¢

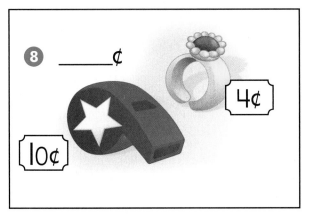

8 _____¢   4¢   10¢

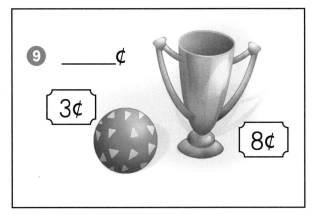

9 _____¢   3¢   8¢

10 **Extended Response** Aisha has $20. Can she buy

3 things? _____ Which items can Aisha buy?

_____

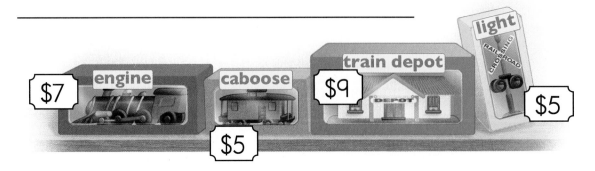

$7   engine   caboose   train depot $9   light $5

$5

Game Play the **Pennies, Nickels, and Dimes Game.**

Note to Home Students calculate costs of combinations of items.

Name _____ Date _____

Exploring Addition Facts

Fill in each chart with different names for the number at the top. You may use cube trains.

1

9		
4	+	5
6	+	3
	+	

2

10		
5	+	5
1	+	9
	+	

3

11		
	+	
	+	
	+	

4

7		
	+	
	+	
	+	

5

12		
	+	
	+	
	+	

6

15		
	+	
	+	
	+	

Note to Home Students use manipulatives to create different representations of the same number.

Textbook This lesson is available in the *eTextbook*.

Fill in each chart with different names for the number at the top. You may use cube trains.

7

12				
5	+	5	+	2
4	+	4	+	4
	+		+	
	+		+	

8

8				
	+		+	
	+		+	
	+		+	
	+		+	

9

10				
	+		+	
	+		+	
	+		+	

10

11				
	+		+	
	+		+	
	+		+	

11

6				
	+		+	
	+		+	
	+		+	

12

15				
	+		+	
	+		+	
	+		+	

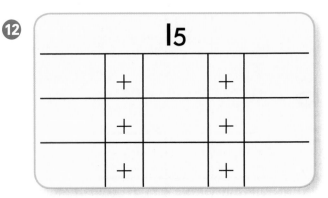

Note to Home Students use manipulatives to create different representations of the same number.

Real Math • Chapter 6 • Lesson 8

LESSON 6.9 **Addition Facts and Money**

Write to show 10 plus a number. Then find the sum. The first one has been done for you.

1

10 + __2__ = __12__

2

10 + ____ = ____

3

10 + ____ = ____

4

10 + ____ = ____

5

10 + ____ = ____

6

10 + ____ = ____

Note to Home Students use coins to model addition with sums to 20.

Textbook This lesson is available in the *eTextbook*.

Add. Use play money if you need to.

7 $6 + 6 =$ _____

8 $6 + 5 =$ _____

9 $6 + 4 =$ _____

10 $1 + 9 =$ _____

11 $2 + 8 =$ _____

12 $3 + 7 =$ _____

13 $10 + 10 =$ _____

14 $10 + 9 =$ _____

15
$$\begin{array}{r} 10 \\ + 8 \\ \hline \end{array}$$

16
$$\begin{array}{r} 8 \\ + 8 \\ \hline \end{array}$$

17
$$\begin{array}{r} 8 \\ + 9 \\ \hline \end{array}$$

18
$$\begin{array}{r} 8 \\ + 7 \\ \hline \end{array}$$

19
$$\begin{array}{r} 6 \\ + 5 \\ \hline \end{array}$$

20
$$\begin{array}{r} 6 \\ + 6 \\ \hline \end{array}$$

21
$$\begin{array}{r} 3 \\ + 9 \\ \hline \end{array}$$

22
$$\begin{array}{r} 3 \\ + 10 \\ \hline \end{array}$$

23
$$\begin{array}{r} 8 \\ + 1 \\ \hline \end{array}$$

24
$$\begin{array}{r} 8 \\ + 2 \\ \hline \end{array}$$

25
$$\begin{array}{r} 7 \\ + 2 \\ \hline \end{array}$$

26
$$\begin{array}{r} 6 \\ + 2 \\ \hline \end{array}$$

Note to Home Students use money to find sums up to 20.

Name _____

Date _____

LESSON 6.10

The Paper Explorer

0	1	2	3	4	5	6	7	8	9	10

Use the Paper Explorer to find the sums.

1 $6 + 5 = 11$

2 $8 + 7 = 15$

3 $7 + 6 = 13$

4 $5 + 9 = 14$

5 $9 + 9 = 18$

6 $8 + 8 = 16$

Note to Home Students notice relationships between the basic addition facts while using the Paper Explorer to find sums. Students see, for instance, that $8 + 8$ is equivalent to $9 + 7$, which is equivalent to $10 + 6$, or 16.

eTextbook This lesson is available in the *eTextbook*.

Counters can be used to find sums.

Use this page to regroup numbers and
find their sums.

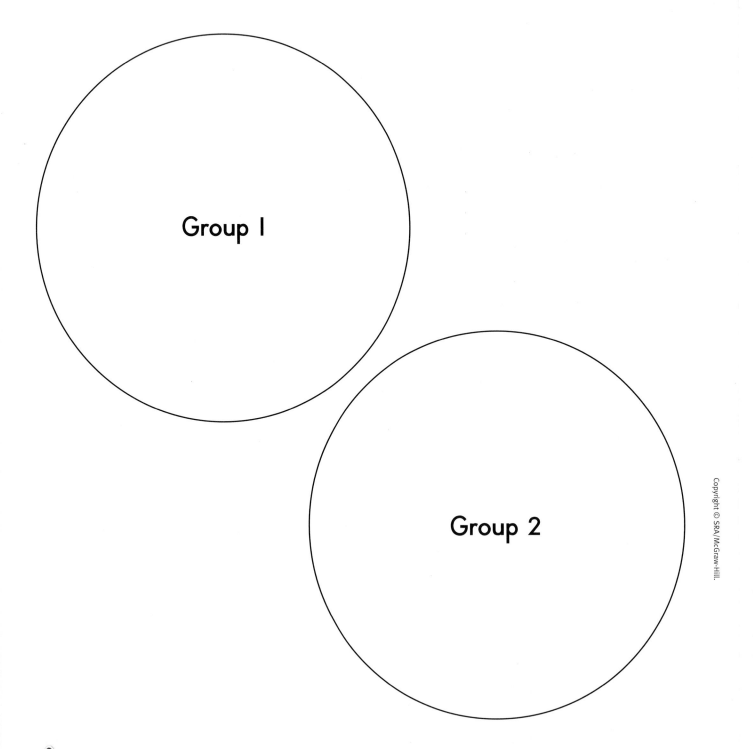

Group 1

Group 2

Note to Home Students find sums by moving counters between circles until they can
represent an addition fact (such as 8 + 8) as 10 plus a number (such as $10 + 6$, or 16).

LESSON
6.11

Addition Facts—Near Doubles

Add to find the sums for these doubles
and near-doubles facts.

1 6 + 6 = _____

2 6 + 7 = _____

3 7 + 7 = _____

4 7 + 6 = _____

5 6 + 5 = _____

6 7 + 8 = _____

7 5 + 5 = _____

8 5 + 4 = _____

9 8 + 8 = _____

10 8 + 9 = _____

11 9 + 8 = _____

12 8 + 7 = _____

13
$$\begin{array}{r} 4 \\ + 4 \\ \hline \end{array}$$

14
$$\begin{array}{r} 3 \\ + 3 \\ \hline \end{array}$$

15
$$\begin{array}{r} 3 \\ + 4 \\ \hline \end{array}$$

16
$$\begin{array}{r} 4 \\ + 3 \\ \hline \end{array}$$

17
$$\begin{array}{r} 9 \\ + 9 \\ \hline \end{array}$$

18
$$\begin{array}{r} 9 \\ + 8 \\ \hline \end{array}$$

19
$$\begin{array}{r} 9 \\ + 10 \\ \hline \end{array}$$

20
$$\begin{array}{r} 10 \\ + 9 \\ \hline \end{array}$$

Note to Home Students find the sums of doubles facts and near-doubles facts.

📘 **Textbook** This lesson is available in the *eTextbook*.

Listen and discuss.

21 Juliet sent 5 letters. Her sister, Helena, also sent 5 letters. Their sister Eliza sent 1 letter. How many letters did the sisters send?

22 Emily spent $9 to buy 3 books. Then she spent some more money to buy 2 more books. How many books did Emily buy? How much money did she spend on the books?

23 Triangle Park has 3 sides. One side is 3 miles long, one side is 4 miles long, and the third side is 5 miles long. If you ride your bike around the park, about how far will you ride?

24 Tickets to the circus are $5 each. If you buy 3 tickets, you save $2. Manuel bought 3 tickets. How much did that cost?

 Note to Home Students solve word problems.

The Remaining Addition Facts

Write addition sentences to make each
sum. Do each a different way.

1 ____ + ____ = 15

2 ____ + ____ = 15

3 ____ + ____ = 15

4 ____ + ____ = 15

5 ____ + ____ = 13

6 ____ + ____ = 13

7 ____ + ____ = 13

8 ____ + ____ = 13

9 ____ + ____ = 16

10 ____ + ____ = 16

11 ____ + ____ = 16

12 ____ + ____ = 16

13 ____ + ____ = 14

14 ____ + ____ = 14

15 ____ + ____ = 14

16 ____ + ____ = 14

Note to Home Students review equivalent addition facts.

Textbook This lesson is available in the *eTextbook*.

Speed Test

1 $0 + 1 =$ ____

2 $10 + 5 =$ ____

3 $4 + 2 =$ ____

4 $8 + 6 =$ ____

5 $5 + 5 =$ ____

6 $6 + 6 =$ ____

7 $9 + 2 =$ ____

8 $3 + 0 =$ ____

9 $7 + 5 =$ ____

10 $6 + 4 =$ ____

11 $7 + 0 =$ ____

12 $10 + 10 =$ ____

13 $5 + 1 =$ ____

14 $5 + 3 =$ ____

15 $8 + 8 =$ ____

16 $10 + 7 =$ ____

17 $\begin{array}{r} 5 \\ + 8 \\ \hline \end{array}$

18 $\begin{array}{r} 8 \\ + 3 \\ \hline \end{array}$

19 $\begin{array}{r} 1 \\ + 3 \\ \hline \end{array}$

20 $\begin{array}{r} 10 \\ + 3 \\ \hline \end{array}$

21 $\begin{array}{r} 2 \\ + 0 \\ \hline \end{array}$

22 $\begin{array}{r} 5 \\ + 8 \\ \hline \end{array}$

23 $\begin{array}{r} 6 \\ + 9 \\ \hline \end{array}$

24 $\begin{array}{r} 8 \\ + 1 \\ \hline \end{array}$

25 $\begin{array}{r} 3 \\ + 4 \\ \hline \end{array}$

Name _____ Date _____

Listen to the problem.

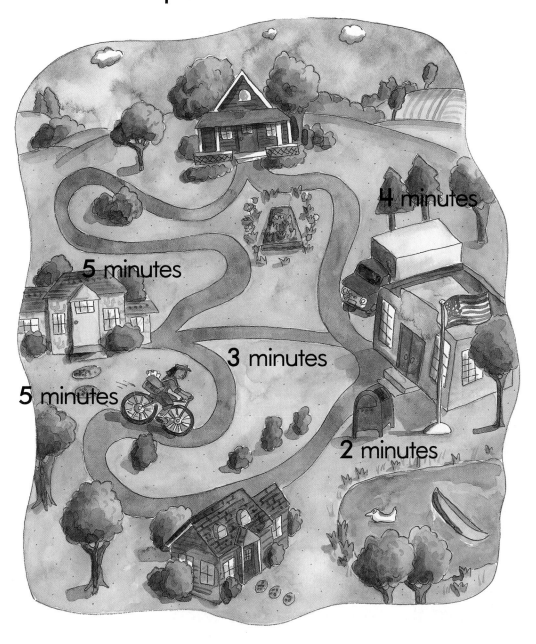

Show the shortest way.

What is her total riding time? _____

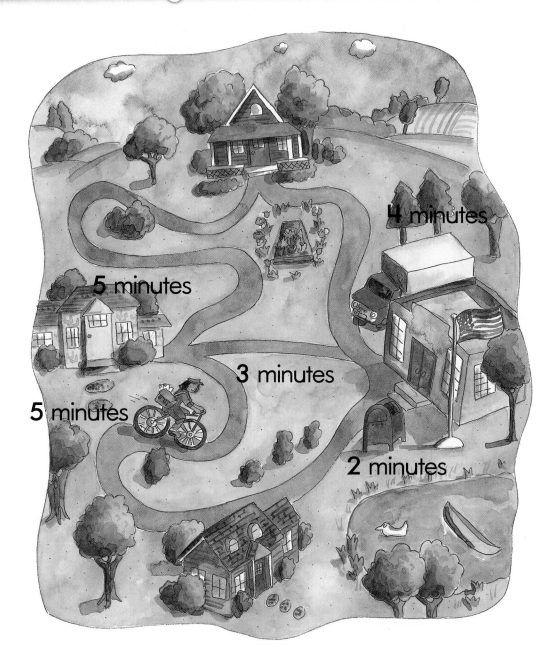

Show the shortest way if Mrs. York had to start at the red house, visit each house, and end at the post office.

What is her total riding time? _____

Cumulative Review

Name _____ Date _____

Pennies and Nickels Lesson 5.1

Draw coins to make the correct amount. Use nickels whenever you can.

 **1** 9¢

 **2** 5¢

 **3** 3¢

....

What Numbers Come Before and After? Lesson 2.3

Fill in the missing numbers.

4 13 14 15 ☐ 17 18 ☐ 20

5 8 ☐ 10 11 ☐ 13 14

6 10 11 12 13 ☐ 15 16 17

....

Adding 10 and Adding 9 Lesson 6.3

7
  6
+ 9
___

8
  10
+ 2
___

9
  9
+ 1
___

10
  10
+ 9
___

Cumulative Review

Function Machines I, II, and III **Lessons 5.9–5.11**

Fill in the blanks.

11

in → out	
5	3
6	4
8	6
9	

The rule is ____

12

in → out	
7	10
	8
1	4
0	

The rule is ____

13

in → out	
5	2
8	5
	4
10	

The rule is ____

Mental Subtraction **Lesson 5.8**

Subtract.

14 6 − 4 = ____   **15** 9 − 3 = ____   **16** 10 − 5 = ____

The Order Law of Addition **Lesson 4.3**

The number tells how many fish are behind the rock. Write how many fish there are in all.

17

18

19

20

Name _____ Date _____

Lessons 6.1–6.3 **Add.** You may use your Addition Table.

1 $0 + 7 =$ ____

5 $10 + 6 =$ ____

2 $5 + 1 =$ ____

6 $7 + 9 =$ ____

3 $3 + 1 =$ ____

7 $8 + 2 =$ ____

4 $4 + 4 =$ ____

8 $9 + 8 =$ ____

Lesson 6.4 **Fill** in the missing numbers.

9

5		7	
	10		

10

6			7
		10	

Fill in the sum for each exercise.

11 $9 + 9 =$ ____

13 $6 + 6 =$ ____

12 $3 + 3 =$ ____

Lesson 6.6 **Listen.** **Then solve.**

⑭ Tom ate 4 oranges. Judy ate 3 oranges. How many oranges were there to start?

_____

Lesson 6.7 **Draw** coins to make 20¢. **Try to do it with:**

⑮ 2 coins

⑯ 4 coins

Lesson 6.9 **Find** the sum.

⑰

$10 + \text{\_\_\_\_} = \text{\_\_\_\_}$

⑱ $7 + 5 = \text{\_\_\_\_}$ ㉑ $6 + 8 = \text{\_\_\_\_}$

⑲ $9 + 8 = \text{\_\_\_\_}$ ㉒ $4 + 9 = \text{\_\_\_\_}$

⑳ $6 + 9 = \text{\_\_\_\_}$ ㉓ $5 + 4 = \text{\_\_\_\_}$

Practice Test

Name _____ Date _____

Add.

1 2 + 3 = _____

2 5 + 2 = _____

3 5 + 5 = _____

4 4 + 5 = _____

5 7 + 1 = _____

6 1 + 0 = _____

Add more addition facts.

7 3 + 10 = _____

8 0 + 10 = _____

9 10 + 4 = _____

10 6 + 10 = _____

11 7 + 10 = _____

12 10 + 3 = _____

13 8 + 6 = _____

14 7 + 7 = _____

15
$$\begin{array}{r} 7 \\ + 4 \\ \hline \end{array}$$

16
$$\begin{array}{r} 9 \\ + 5 \\ \hline \end{array}$$

Solve.

⑰ Amanda is 5 years old. Thad is 4 years older than Amanda. How old is Thad?

  a. 1   **b.** 5   **c.** 4   **d.** 9

⑱ Tito is 3 years younger than Anya. Anya is 4 years older than Meg. Meg is 9 years old. How old is Tito?

  a. 10   **b.** 3   **c.** 9   **d.** 4

⑲ Son Yei has 5 pennies more than Terrance. Son Yei has 3 pennies more than Juan. Juan has 5 pennies. How many pennies does Terrance have?

  a. 8   **b.** 4   **c.** 3   **d.** 5

Subtract.

⑳ − 4 = _____

  a. 2   **b.** 6   **c.** 4   **d.** 10

㉑ − 3 = _____

  a. 9   **b.** 6   **c.** 3   **d.** 12

㉒   9
   − 7
  ─────

  a. 4   **b.** 5   **c.** 16   **d.** 2

Practice Test

Name _____ Date _____

Add.

23   6
       + 4

a. 4   **b.** 5

c. 10   **d.** 2

24   6
       + 7

a. 12   **b.** 13

c. 6   **d.** 1

25   8
       + 8

a. 8   **b.** 0

c. 16   **d.** 15

26   8
       + 2

a. 10   **b.** 6

c. 9   **d.** 8

Add to find how much each pair would cost.

27

a. 5   **b.** 18

c. 7   **d.** 19

28

a. 4   **b.** 12

c. 11   **d.** 10

Extended Response **Write** addition sentences for the cube train.

Make each addition different.

29

____ + ____ = 15

____ + ____ = 15

____ + ____ = 15

____ + ____ + ____ = 15

____ + ____ + ____ = 15

Extended Response **Write** addition sentences for 12.

Make each addition different.

30 ____ + ____ = 12

____ + ____ = 12

____ + ____ = 12

____ + ____ + ____ = 12

____ + ____ + ____ = 12

Name _____ Date _____

Thinking Story

The Third House on Fungo Street

Count the number of houses on Fungo Street. Write the number. _____

🎒 **Note to Home** Students listen to the Thinking Story "The Third House on Fungo Street" and answer questions about the story.

📺 **Textbook** This lesson is available in the *eTextbook*.

Color the first house blue.

Color the second house green.

Color the fourth house red.

Color the last house yellow.

Color the third house any color you want!

More Subtraction Facts

In This Chapter You Will Learn

- more ways to do subtraction exercises.

Name _____ Date _____

Listen to the problem.

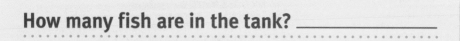

How many fish are in the tank? _____

 How do you know? _____

LESSON 7.1 Missing Addends I

Look at your *Number Strips.*

❶ Draw the missing squares.

5	7	8	6	4	3	9	7

🎒 **Note to Home** Students use their *Number Strips* to find missing addends.

ⓔ **Textbook** This lesson is available in the *eTextbook.*

Add or subtract. You may use the number line. Be sure to watch the signs.

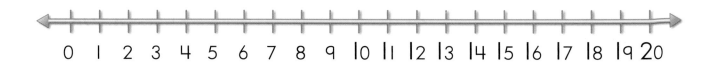

0 1 2 3 4 5 6 7 8 9 10 11 12 13 14 15 16 17 18 19 20

17 $4 + 5 = $ _____   **18** $6 + 3 = $ _____

19 $9 - 5 = $ _____   **20** $10 - 5 = $ _____

21 $10 + 0 = $ _____   **22** $10 - 10 = $ _____

23 $5 + 6 = $ _____   **24** $3 + 3 = $ _____

25 $6 - 3 = $ _____   **26** $8 + 8 = $ _____

27 $16 - 8 = $ _____   **28** $7 - 7 = $ _____

Listen, and then discuss and solve.

29 **Extended Response** Bai had 6 bracelets. Then she bought 4 more bracelets and gave 2 of them to Kara. Now how many bracelets does Bai have? _____
How did you solve this? _____

_____

🎒 **Note to Home** Students add and subtract using the number line.

LESSON 7.5 Subtracting Special Facts

Listen, and discuss. Then write a number sentence.

❶ Alicia is 10 years old. How old was she 9 years ago? _____

_____

❷ Martin had $8. He spent some money on fish, and now he has $5. How much money did Martin spend? _____

_____

❸ Adrianna planted 12 bean seeds. Later, 10 of them sprouted, and 5 of them grew fast. How many of the bean seeds did not sprout? _____

_____

❹ Michael had 10 sports cards. Then he gave 2 of them to Wolfgang and 1 to Alice. Now how many sports cards does he have? _____

_____

⎙ **Note to Home** Students solve word problems and then write a corresponding number sentence.

Subtract.

⑤ 10 − 10 = _____

⑥ 9 − 9 = _____

⑦ 7 − 2 = _____

⑧ 9 − 3 = _____

⑨ 10 − 2 = _____

⑩ 13 − 10 = _____

⑪ 3 − 1 = _____

⑫ 6 − 6 = _____

⑬ 6 − 5 = _____

⑭ 10 − 9 = _____

⑮ 7 − 0 = _____

⑯ 12 − 3 = _____

⑰ 10 − 8 = _____

⑱ 8 − 7 = _____

⑲ 5 − 4 = _____

⑳ 12 − 10 = _____

🎒 **Note to Home** Students do subtraction exercises.

Real Math • Chapter 7 • Lesson 5

Name _____ Date _____

Aaron has 14 cans of dog food.

He uses 3 cans each day.

When will he run out?

 Hailey is making a table to solve the problem.

Steve is drawing a picture to solve the problem.

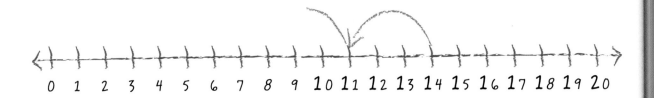

0 1 2 3 4 5 6 7 8 9 10 11 12 13 14 15 16 17 18 19 20

 Show how you solved the problem.

Aaron will run out of dog food on _____.

Cumulative Review

Name _____ Date _____

Measuring Height Lesson 3.4

Color the tallest red. Color the shortest blue. Color the others any color.

1

2

Adding with Hidden Counters Lesson 4.2

How many altogether?

3

4

5

6

Adding 5 Lesson 5.4

Write the number sentences.

7 5 + ☐ = 9

8 5 + ☐ = 7

9 ☐ + ☐ = 10

10 ☐ + ☐ = 5

Copyright © SRA/McGraw-Hill.

Cumulative Review

+	0	1	2	3	4	5	6	7	8	9	10
0	0	1	2	3	4	5	6	7	8	9	10
1	1	2	3	4	5	6	7	8	9	10	11
2	2	3	4	5	6	7	8	9	10	11	12
3	3	4	5	6	7	8	9	10	11	12	13
4	4	5	6	7	8	9	10	11	12	13	14
5	5	6	7	8	9	10	11	12	13	14	15
6	6	7	8	9	10	11	12	13	14	15	16
7	7	8	9	10	11	12	13	14	15	16	17
8	8	9	10	11	12	13	14	15	16	17	18
9	9	10	11	12	13	14	15	16	17	18	19
10	10	11	12	13	14	15	16	17	18	19	20

Progress on the Addition Table Lesson 6.6

Use the addition table to find each sum.

⑪ $10 + 1 =$ _____   ⑫ $2 + 5 =$ _____   ⑬ $7 + 7 =$ _____

⑭ $9 + 5 =$ _____   ⑮ $0 + 10 =$ _____   ⑯ $1 + 8 =$ _____

⑰ $\begin{array}{r} 6 \\ + 6 \\ \hline \end{array}$ ⑱ $\begin{array}{r} 6 \\ + 7 \\ \hline \end{array}$ ⑲ $\begin{array}{r} 6 \\ + 8 \\ \hline \end{array}$

Missing Addends I Lesson 7.1

Listen and then solve.

⑳ Mary needs 8 cents but she only has 5¢.
   How many more cents does she need?

   _____

LESSON 7.6 Subtracting 10, 9, and 8

Listen, and discuss.

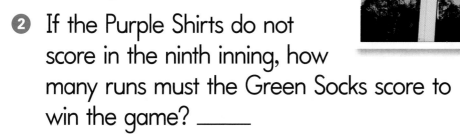

1. At the end of eight innings the score was Purple Shirts 14 and Green Socks 9. By how many runs were the Purple Shirts winning? _____

2. If the Purple Shirts do not score in the ninth inning, how many runs must the Green Socks score to win the game? _____

3. If the Green Socks score 5 more runs, which team will be winning? _____

4. In the ninth inning, the Purple Shirts scored 1 run, and the Green Socks scored 4 runs. What was the final score? _____

Subtract.

5. $15 - 10 =$ _____

6. $15 - 5 =$ _____

7. $15 - 6 =$ _____

8. $15 - 9 =$ _____

9. $14 - 4 =$ _____

10. $14 - 5 =$ _____

🎒 **Note to Home** Students solve word problems and do subtraction exercises.

Ⓔ **Textbook** This lesson is available in the *eTextbook*.

Subtract.

11 $14 - 9 = \underline{\hspace{1cm}}$

12 $14 - 10 = \underline{\hspace{1cm}}$

13 $17 - 9 = \underline{\hspace{1cm}}$

14 $17 - 10 = \underline{\hspace{1cm}}$

15 $17 - 7 = \underline{\hspace{1cm}}$

16 $17 - 8 = \underline{\hspace{1cm}}$

17 $19 - 9 = \underline{\hspace{1cm}}$

18 $19 - 10 = \underline{\hspace{1cm}}$

19 $18 - 8 = \underline{\hspace{1cm}}$

20 $16 - 7 = \underline{\hspace{1cm}}$

21 $16 - 9 = \underline{\hspace{1cm}}$

22 $16 - 10 = \underline{\hspace{1cm}}$

23 $16 - 6 = \underline{\hspace{1cm}}$

24 $13 - 3 = \underline{\hspace{1cm}}$

25 $13 - 10 = \underline{\hspace{1cm}}$

26 $13 - 4 = \underline{\hspace{1cm}}$

27 $13 - 9 = \underline{\hspace{1cm}}$

28 $12 - 3 = \underline{\hspace{1cm}}$

29 $12 - 10 = \underline{\hspace{1cm}}$

30 $10 - 10 = \underline{\hspace{1cm}}$

Note to Home Students do subtraction exercises.

LESSON 7.7 Subtraction Facts Related to the Doubles

Listen, and discuss. Then write a number sentence if you can.

1 Manuel is 13 years old. He studied 4 hours on Monday and 4 hours on Tuesday. How many hours did he study both days?

_____

2 Allie is 10 years old. She was at school 5 hours on Monday. Then she was at school some more hours on Tuesday. How many hours was Allie at school both days?

_____

3 Tisha wanted to bake 16 loaves of bread. She baked 8 of them. How many more must she bake?

_____

4 Aaron was downloading a program. It was supposed to take 8 minutes. So far he has waited 2 minutes. About how many more minutes will it take?

_____

 Note to Home Students solve word problems.

e Textbook This lesson is available in the *eTextbook.*

Add or subtract.

5 $3 + 3 \ = \ \rule{2cm}{0.4pt}$

6 $6 - 3 \ = \ \rule{2cm}{0.4pt}$

7 $6 - 2 \ = \ \rule{2cm}{0.4pt}$

8 $6 - 4 \ = \ \rule{2cm}{0.4pt}$

9 $7 + 7 \ = \ \rule{2cm}{0.4pt}$

10 $14 - 7 \ = \ \rule{2cm}{0.4pt}$

11 $14 - 8 \ = \ \rule{2cm}{0.4pt}$

12 $5 + 5 \ = \ \rule{2cm}{0.4pt}$

13 $10 - 5 \ = \ \rule{2cm}{0.4pt}$

14 $9 + 9 \ = \ \rule{2cm}{0.4pt}$

15 $18 - 9 \ = \ \rule{2cm}{0.4pt}$

16 $18 - 10 \ = \ \rule{2cm}{0.4pt}$

17 $18 - 8 \ = \ \rule{2cm}{0.4pt}$

18 $8 + 8 \ = \ \rule{2cm}{0.4pt}$

19 $16 - 8 \ = \ \rule{2cm}{0.4pt}$

20 $16 - 10 \ = \ \rule{2cm}{0.4pt}$

Note to Home Students do addition and subtraction exercises.

Real Math • Chapter 7 • Lesson 7

LESSON 7.8 — The Remaining Subtraction Facts

Listen, and discuss.

1 Marta has 8 puppies. Some of them are hiding behind the couch. How many are behind the couch?

2 Brandon has $10. Does he have enough money to ride the go-carts once, play miniature golf once, and play a video game? _____ Explain how you know.

Go-carts $4

Miniature golf . . $3

Video game $1

Bumper boats . . $3

3 If Brandon rides the bumper boats twice, plays miniature golf once, and plays one video game, how much change will he get? _____ Explain how you know.

4 Each football team scored 9 points during the game. How many points were scored by both teams? _____

 Note to Home Students solve word problems.

Game

Play Subtracto

0	1	2	3	4	5	6	7	8	9	10

0	1	2	3	4	5	6	7	8	9	10

0	1	2	3	4	5	6	7	8	9	10

0	1	2	3	4	5	6	7	8	9	10

Players:
Two

Materials:

- Two 0–5 *Number Cubes* and two 5–10 *Number Cubes*

- A different color crayon for each player

HOW TO PLAY

1. Both players use the above game form. Players use only one line at a time.

2. On each turn, the player chooses to roll any two cubes and subtracts the smaller number from the greater number. The player colors that box in his or her color. If a box is already taken, the player loses his or her turn.

3. The first player to fill 6 boxes in his or her color is the winner.

4. Students can replay the game using the next line.

LESSON 7.9 Inequalities and Equalities I

14   < 17

Draw >, <, or = between each pair of numbers.

1. 4 ◯ 7   2. 10 ◯ 9   3. 5 ◯ 5

4. 6 ◯ 7   5. 2 ◯ 2   6. 2 ◯ 0

7. 0 ◯ 10   8. 5 ◯ 4   9. 14 ◯ 9

10. 11 ◯ 15   11. 18 ◯ 9   12. 18 ◯ 18

Note to Home Students use relation signs.

eTextbook This lesson is available in the *eTextbook*.

13 Ring each number that is greater than 6.

7   4   6   5   9   1   8

14 Ring each sum that is greater than 10.

4	5	6	7	8	9	10
+ 2	+ 2	+ 2	+ 2	+ 2	+ 2	+ 2

15 Ring each number that is less than 12.

8   6   14   11   15   9

16 Ring each sum that is less than 14.

8 + 9
8 + 8
8 + 7
8 + 6
8 + 5
8 + 4

17 Ring each sum that is 13.

10 + 3
9 + 4
8 + 5
8 + 6
8 + 7
8 + 8

LESSON 7.10 Inequalities and Equalities II

Draw the correct sign. Draw >, <, or =.

1. $12 + 4$ ◯ 14

2. $12 + 3$ ◯ 14

3. $12 + 2$ ◯ 14

4. $12 + 1$ ◯ 14

5. $12 + 0$ ◯ 14

6. 15 ◯ $9 + 3$

7. 15 ◯ $9 + 4$

8. 15 ◯ $9 + 5$

9. 15 ◯ $9 + 6$

10. 15 ◯ $10 + 5$

11. $8 + 8$ ◯ 16

12. $8 + 7$ ◯ 16

13. $8 + 9$ ◯ 16

14. $8 + 10$ ◯ 16

15. $8 + 11$ ◯ 16

16. 18 ◯ $9 + 9$

17. 17 ◯ $9 + 9$

18. 16 ◯ $9 + 8$

19. 16 ◯ $8 + 8$

20. 16 ◯ $8 + 7$

Note to Home Students use relation signs.

Textbook This lesson is available in the *eTextbook*.

Draw the correct sign. Draw >, <, or =.

21 5 + 5 ◯ 5 + 4   **22** 5 + 6 ◯ 5 + 5

23 5 + 7 ◯ 5 + 6   **24** 5 + 8 ◯ 8 + 5

25 5 + 9 ◯ 5 + 10   **26** 3 + 4 ◯ 4 + 3

27 5 + 4 ◯ 4 + 5   **28** 6 + 9 ◯ 9 + 6

29 7 + 8 ◯ 7 + 9   **30** 7 + 9 ◯ 7 + 8

31 7 + 7 ◯ 7 + 6   **32** 8 + 8 ◯ 8 + 7

33 8 + 8 ◯ 8 + 9   **34** 9 + 8 ◯ 8 + 9

35 10 + 9 ◯ 10 + 8   **36** 85 + 1 ◯ 85 + 3

37 76 + 3 ◯ 73 + 1   **38** 65 + 3 ◯ 64 + 3

39 56 + 10 ◯ 46 + 10   **40** 75 + 9 ◯ 85 + 9

Note to Home Students use relation signs.

Name _____ Date _____

Listen to the problem.

How many fish did Paige start with? _____

How do you know? _____

_____

_____

Nick also has a fish tank.

How many fish did Nick start with? _____

How do you know? _____

_____

_____

Cumulative Review

Name _____ Date _____

Counting with the Monthly Calendar Lesson 1.10

Answer the questions.

1 Is October 4 a Wednesday? _____

2 Is October 28 a Tuesday? _____

3 How many Fridays are there? _____

October						
SUN	MON	TUE	WED	THU	FRI	SAT
1	2	3	4	5	6	7
8	9	10	11	12	13	14
15	16	17	18	19	20	21
22	23	24	25	26	27	28
29	30	31				

The Order Law of Addition Lesson 4.3

The number tells how many fish are behind the rock.

Write how many fish there are altogether.

4

5

6

7

Copyright © SRA/McGraw-Hill.

e **Textbook** This lesson is available in the *eTextbook*.

261

Cumulative Review

Estimating and Comparing Length I Lesson 3.2

How long? Use your *Number Strips.*

8

——

9

——

10

——

....

Tally Marks Lesson 2.4

How many?

11   **12**   **13**

....

Numbers on a Clock Lesson 1.11

What time is it?

14

———————

15

———————

Chapter Review

Name _____ Date _____

Lesson 7.1 **Look** at your *Number Strips.* Draw the missing squares on these.

① | 9 | | | | |

② | 3 |

③ | 5 | | | |

Lesson 7.2 **Write** how many were added to the can.

④  7 + ☐ = 9   ⑥ 6  + ☐ = 7

⑤  4 + ☐ = 10

Lesson 7.3 **What** numbers are missing? Write them in.

⑦

7	
10	3

7 + ____ = 13   13 − 7 = ____

Lesson 7.5 **Listen.** Then write the number sentence.

⑧ Christoph had $9. He spent some money, and now he has $4. How much money did Christoph spend?

_____

Lesson 7.6 **Subtract.**

⑨ $16 - 10 =$ _____   ⑩ $14 - 5 =$ _____

⑪ $15 - 9 =$ _____   ⑫ $11 - 2 =$ _____

Lesson 7.7 **Add** or subtract.

⑬ $3 + 3 =$ _____   ⑭ $6 - 3 =$ _____

⑮ $6 - 2 =$ _____   ⑯ $6 - 4 =$ _____

Lessons 7.9–7.10 **Draw >, <, or = between each pair of numbers.**

⑰ 4 ☐ 7   ⑱ 18 ☐ 18

⑲ 13 ☐ 17

Name _____ Date _____

Solve.

1. Nancy needs to earn 9 merit badges. She has already earned 7 merit badges. How many more does she need to earn? _____

2. Brianna has 4 new books to read. She reads 3 of the books. How many books does she have left to read? _____

3. Raul had 13 baseballs cards. He gave some away and had 6 left. How many baseball cards did Raul give away? _____

Write how many were added.

4.
$+$_____ $= 9$

5.
$+$_____ $= 7$

6.
$+$_____ $= 15$

Practice Test

Ring the correct rule.

7

in	out
9	7
4	2
6	4
5	3

a. −1
b. −2
c. +2
d. +1

8

in	out
10	11
6	7
3	4
9	10

a. −1
b. +2
c. +1
d. −2

9

in	out
10	5
8	3
6	1
7	2

a. −5
b. +5
c. +1
d. −1

Add the doubles.

10 $5 + 5 =$ _____

a. 6   b. 5   c. 0   d. 10

11 $9 + 9 =$ _____

a. 18   b. 9   c. 0   d. 17

12 $3 + 3 =$ _____

a. 3   b. 0   c. 6   d. 5

Name _____   Date _____

Subtract.

13 $12 - 6 = $ _____

a. 12 b. 5 c. 6 d. 7

14 $14 - 7 = $ _____

a. 7 b. 8 c. 6 d. 2

15 $17 - 8 = $ _____

a. 10 b. 8 c. 7 d. 9

Ring the number to make the sentence true.

16 $7 + 4 > $ _____

a. 15 b. 10 c. 12 d. 14

17 $2 + 7 < $ _____

a. 14 b. 5 c. 6 d. 8

18 $3 + 10 = $ _____

a. 15 b. 8 c. 13 d. 19

Practice Test

Extended Response **Write** 3 different facts to make each sentence true.

19 $10 + 4 <$ _____ $+$ _____

$10 + 4 <$ _____ $+$ _____

$10 + 4 <$ _____ $+$ _____

20 $2 + 11 >$ _____ $+$ _____

$2 + 11 >$ _____ $+$ _____

$2 + 11 >$ _____ $+$ _____

21 $8 + 6 =$ _____ $+$ _____

$8 + 6 =$ _____ $+$ _____

$8 + 6 =$ _____ $+$ _____

22 $9 + 7 >$ _____ $+$ _____

$9 + 7 >$ _____ $+$ _____

$9 + 7 >$ _____ $+$ _____

How Deep Is the Water?

Ring the correct answer.

Is the fish taller than or shorter than the man?

    taller than   shorter than

Is the fish taller than or shorter than the woman?

    taller than   shorter than

Note to Home Students listen to the Thinking Story "How Deep is the Water?" and answer questions about the story.

Textbook This lesson is available in the *eTextbook*.

Help the fish find its way back to the school.

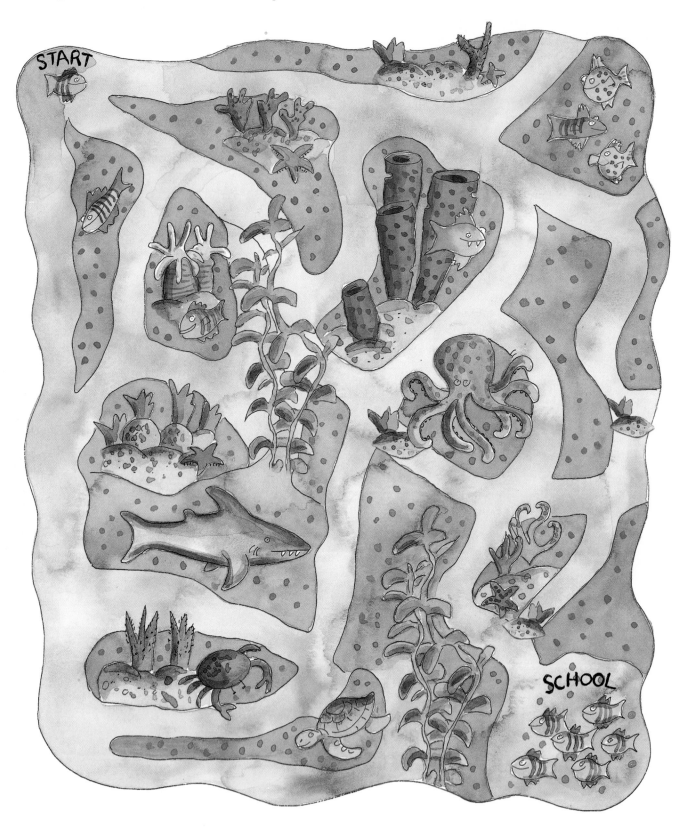

In This Chapter You Will Learn
- more about finger sets.
- about more addition and subtraction facts.
- more about functions.

Problem Solving

Name _____ Date _____

Listen to the problem.
Draw your new room.

How do you know your room has 10 ⬜⬜⬜⬜⬜ ? _____

LESSON 8.1 Ordinal Numbers

first second third fourth fifth sixth seventh eighth ninth tenth

Color the correct picture.

1 The second pumpkin

2 The tenth chick

3 The sixth mug

4 The eighth ball

5 The fourth pencil

Note to Home Students use ordinal numbers to identify objects in a sequence.

Textbook This lesson is available in the *eTextbook*.

December

Sunday	Monday	Tuesday	Wednesday	Thursday	Friday	Saturday
					1	2
3	4	5	6	7	8	9
10	11	12	13	14	15	16
17	18	19	20	21	22	23
24 / 31	25	26	27	28	29	30

Look at the calendar. Answer the questions.

6 What is the first Wednesday?   December _____

7 What is the second Saturday?   December _____

8 What is the third Tuesday?   December _____

9 What is the last day of the month? December _____

10 **Extended Response** Maya earns 5¢ for doing chores every Friday. How much money will she earn in December? Show how you know. _____

_____

 Note to Home Students use ordinal numbers to describe dates on the calendar.

Name _____ Date _____

LESSON 8.2 **Finger Sets to 40**

1

How many fingers? ☐

2

How many fingers? ☐

3

How many fingers? ☐

🔒 **Note to Home** Students count finger sets for numbers 0 to 40.

ⓔ **Textbook** This lesson is available in the *eTextbook*.

Fill in the missing numbers.

0	1	2	3		5	6		8	9
10		12	13	14		16	17	18	
20	21		23	24	25		27		29
30		32	33		35	36	37	38	39
40									

Game Play the **From 20 to 40 by 1 or 2 Game.**

Note to Home Students sequence numbers 0 to 40 by filling in the chart.

Name _____ Date _____

How many cents?

1   _____ ¢

2   _____ ¢

3   _____ ¢

4   _____ ¢

5    _____ ¢

6   _____ ¢

7   _____ ¢

 Note to Home Students use coins to form amounts to 40¢.

e Textbook This lesson is available in the *eTextbook*.

Use coins to make the correct amount.
Draw the coins. Then draw another way
to make the correct amount.

8 20¢	**9** 20¢
10 25¢	**11** 25¢
12 31¢	**13** 31¢
14 17¢	**15** 17¢

Copyright © SRA/McGraw-Hill.

Note to Home Students use coins to form amounts to 40¢.

LESSON 8.4 Addition with Numbers to 40

  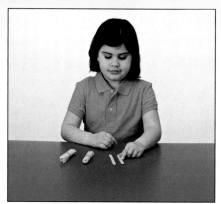

$$18 + 4 = 22$$

Add. Use sticks.

1 $19 + 2 =$ _____

2 $25 + 5 =$ _____

3 $32 + 4 =$ _____

4 $28 + 4 =$ _____

5 $35 + 5 =$ _____

Note to Home Students use concrete manipulatives to do addition with numbers to 40.

Textbook This lesson is available in the *eTextbook*.

There are too many crayons. Ring the correct number of crayons.

6 30   

7 20   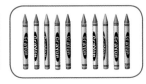

8 10   

9 5   

10 0   

11 15   

Game Play the **Add the Coins Game.**

Note to Home Students count fives and tens to form amounts to 40.

LESSON 8.5 Subtraction with Numbers to 40

$$23 - 5 = 18$$

Subtract. Use sticks.

1 $38 - 4 =$ _____

2 $32 - 5 =$ _____

3 $28 - 10 =$ _____

4 $32 - 3 =$ _____

5 $34 - 15 =$ _____

🎒 **Note to Home** Students use concrete manipulatives to do subtraction with numbers to 40.

📱 **Textbook** This lesson is available in the *eTextbook*.

Add or subtract. You may use sticks.

6 $37 + 2 =$ _____

7 $39 + 3 =$ _____

8 $22 - 5 =$ _____

9 $23 - 4 =$ _____

10 $19 + 2 =$ _____

11 $21 - 2 =$ _____

 **Note to Home** Students use concrete manipulatives to add or subtract with numbers to 40.

Real Math • Chapter 8 • Lesson 5

LESSON 8.6 Counting by Tens

There are 10 sticks in a bundle.

How many sticks altogether?

①

_____

②

_____

③

_____

④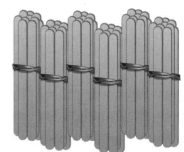

_____

⑤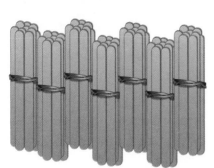

_____

⑥

_____

Note to Home Students count by tens.

e Textbook This lesson is available in the *eTextbook*.

How many tally marks? Ring sets of ten to help you count.

7 ||||| ||||| ||||| ||||| ||||| ||||| ||||| ||||| ||||| ||||| ||||| ||||| _____

8 ||||| ||||| ||||| ||||| ||||| ||||| ||||| ||||| ||||| ||||| _____

9 ||||| ||||| ||||| ||||| ||||| ||||| ||||| ||||| _____

10 ||||| ||||| ||||| ||||| ||||| ||||| _____

11 ||||| ||||| ||||| ||||| _____

12 Make 30 tally marks here.

 Play the **Flea Market Game.**

 Note to Home Students use tally marks to count by tens.

Name _____ Date _____

Listen to the teacher.

Play Treasure Hunt.

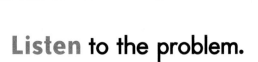
Listen to the problem.

<u>My moves:</u> Down 2, Right 7, Up 2, Left 4, Up 3

Now I am at 45. Where did I start?

 Devin will use Guess, Check, and Adjust.

 Aida will Work Backward.

 Show how you solved the problem.

Cumulative Review

Name _____ Date _____

Pennies and Nickels Lesson 5.1

Draw coins to make the correct amount. Use nickels whenever you can. Use play coins to help.

 **1** 8¢

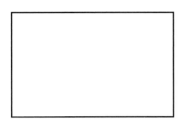

 **2** 6¢

Ordinal Numbers Lesson 8.1

Color the correct picture.

3 The tenth chick

Numbers on a Clock Lesson 1.11

Draw a line between the clocks that tell the same time.

4  2:30

5  1:30

6  4:00

Cumulative Review

The Addition Table Lesson 6.11

Add to find the sums for these doubles and near-doubles facts.

7 6 + 6 = _____   **8** 5 + 5 = _____

9 6 + 7 = _____   **10** 5 + 4 = _____

11 7 + 7 = _____   **12** 8 + 8 = _____

Relating Addition and Subtraction Lesson 7.4

Add or subtract.

13 7 + 2 = _____   **14** 2 + 7 = _____

15 9 − 7 = _____   **16** 9 − 2 = _____

17 6 + 7 = _____   **18** 13 − 7 = _____

Inequalities and Equalites II Lesson 7.10

Draw the correct sign. Draw >, <, or =.

19 15 ◯ 9 + 3   **20** 8 + 8 ◯ 8 + 7

21 75 ◯ 85 + 8   **22** 12 + 2 ◯ 14

23 5 + 5 ◯ 4 + 5   **24** 56 + 10 ◯ 46 + 10

Real Math • Chapter 8

Name _____ Date _____

Numbers to 100

Fill in the missing numbers.

0	1	2		4	5	6	7		9
10	11		13	14		16	17	18	19
20		22	23	24	25	26		28	
30	31			34	35	36	37	38	
	41	42	43	44		46	47	48	
50	51	52	53	54	55		57	58	
60	61	62	63	64	65		67		69
70	71			74	75	76	77	78	79
	81	82	83			86	87	88	89
90			93	94	95	96		98	99
100									

 Note to Home Students practice writing numbers through 100.

e Textbook This lesson is available in the *eTextbook*.

Connect the dots. Start at 75, and count on.

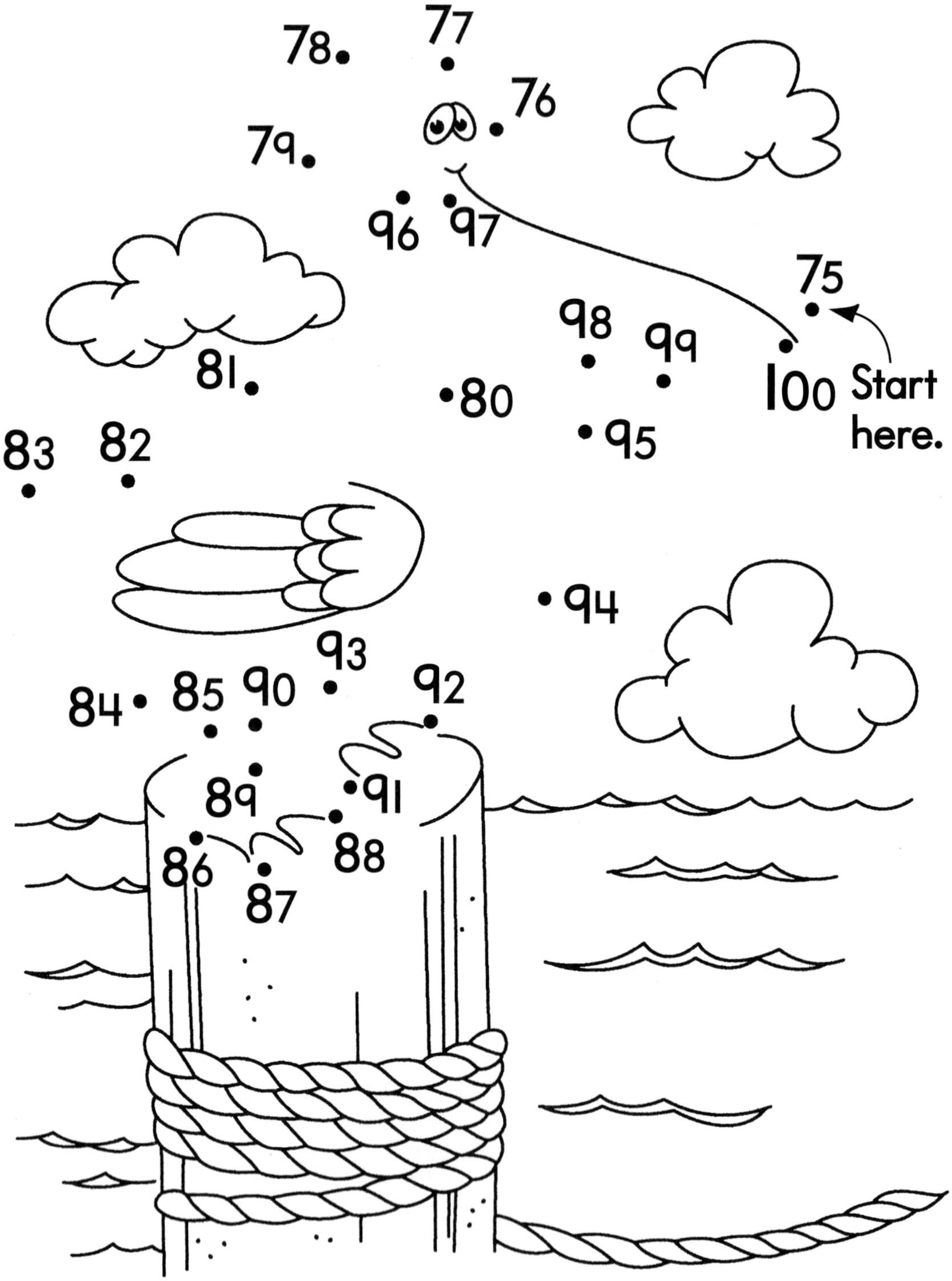

77
78
76
79
96
97
75
98
99
100
Start here.
81
80
95
83
82
94
93
84
85
90
92
89
91
86
88
87

Note to Home Students sequence numbers to 100.

LESSON 8.8 — Adding and Subtracting to 100

Think: how many tens? Then add.

① 50 + 20 = _____   **②** 30 + 30 = _____

③ 60 + 10 = _____   **④** 40 + 40 = _____

⑤ 20 + 20 = _____   **⑥** 50 + 30 = _____

Think: how many tens? Then subtract.

⑦ 40 – 20 = _____   **⑧** 50 – 40 = _____

⑨ 60 – 40 = _____   **⑩** 90 – 20 = _____

⑪ 50 – 30 = _____   **⑫** 80 – 40 = _____

⑬ 70 – 10 = _____   **⑭** 80 – 30 = _____

Note to Home Students add and subtract multiples of ten.

Textbook This lesson is available in the *eTextbook*.

Add or subtract these problems in your head if you can. Use a number table if you need to.

⑮ 42
+ 10

⑯ 42
+ 20

⑰ 42
+ 30

⑱ 55
– 10

⑲ 65
– 10

⑳ 67
+ 20

㉑ 20
– 20

㉒ 31
+ 30

㉓ 31
+ 40

Mrs. Mars is 37 years old.

㉔ How old will she be in 10 years? _____

㉕ How old was she 10 years ago? _____

㉖ In how many years will she be 57 years old? _____

Note to Home Students add and subtract multiples of ten.

Name _____ Date _____

Functions to 100

Fill in the missing number.
Then fill in the rule.

①

in → out	
39	40
51	52
63	
79	80

_____

②

in → out	
80	79
60	59
40	
30	29

_____

③

in → out	
74	78
4	8
5	9
10	

_____

④

in → out	
6	2
74	
69	65
25	21

_____

⑤

in → out	
0	10
10	20
20	30
30	

_____

⑥

in → out	
51	56
37	42
	39
25	30

_____

Fill in the missing number.
Then fill in the rule.

7

in	out
50	30
21	
31	11
29	9

_____

8

in	out
5	11
29	35
	45
71	77

_____

9

in	out
12	6
	7
14	8
15	9

_____

10

in	out
10	19
14	23
24	
34	43

_____

11

in	out
5	35
20	50
21	
70	100

_____

12

in	out
100	90
10	
15	5
71	61

_____

13

in	out
25	25
	35
46	46
72	72

_____

14

in	out
18	16
	14
14	
12	10

_____

15

in	out
17	20
37	40
57	
77	80

_____

🎒 **Note to Home** Students solve function problems.

LESSON 8.10 Identifying Operations

Listen. Then write a number sentence that solves the problem. If there is no number sentence, draw a ?.

1 Manuel is 9 years old. His sister Lola is 6 years old. How much older is Manuel?

_____

2 Danny walked 4 blocks from his home to the library. Then he walked home. How many blocks did Danny walk?

_____

3 Jill had 75 sports cards. Then she bought some more. Now how many does she have?

_____

4 There were 10 students coming to the party. Each needed 1 party hat and 2 napkins. How many napkins were needed?

_____

Note to Home Students solve word problems.

e Textbook This lesson is available in the *eTextbook*.

What is the missing sign? Draw + or −.

⑤ 4 ⬡ 1 = 5

⑥ 3 ⬡ 1 = 2

⑦ 6 ⬡ 1 = 5

⑧ 7 ⬡ 1 = 8

⑨ 37 ⬡ 5 = 42

⑩ 87 ⬡ 10 = 77

⑪ 69 ⬡ 2 = 71

⑫ 29 ⬡ 3 = 26

⑬ 40 ⬡ 10 = 30

⑭ 23 ⬡ 1 = 24

Copyright © SRA/McGraw-Hill.

Note to Home Students select an operation sign to make a true number sentence.

Real Math • Chapter 8 • Lesson 10

LESSON 8.11 Detecting Wrong Answers and Using Relation Signs

Listen. Only one answer is correct.
Ring it and tell how you know.

1 Kevin is 20 years old. How many years old might he be in a few years?

27   15   85

2 Julia had 25 marbles. Then she lost some. Later she bought more than she had lost. Now how many marbles does Julia have?

29   24   25

3 Heike was baking a cake. She used all of the flour she had. Now how many cups of flour does she have?

24   0   74

4 Calvin was 6 years old 10 years ago. How old is Calvin today?

10   4   16

Note to Home Students detect obviously wrong answers.

Textbook This lesson is available in the *eTextbook*.

Draw the correct sign. Draw <, >, or =.

⑤ 6 + 2 ◯ 10   **⑥** 8 + 7 ◯ 10

⑦ 60 + 1 ◯ 70   **⑧** 65 + 10 ◯ 70

⑨ 5 − 2 ◯ 5   **⑩** 14 + 6 ◯ 8

⑪ 5 + 2 ◯ 6   **⑫** 16 − 5 ◯ 17

⑬ 75 − 5 ◯ 70   **⑭** 75 − 6 ◯ 70

⑮ 7 − 2 ◯ 8   **⑯** 7 − 6 ◯ 1

⑰ 85 − 6 ◯ 84   **⑱** 85 − 16 ◯ 84

⑲ 7 + 3 ◯ 5   **⑳** 13 − 4 ◯ 18

🎒 **Note to Home** Students choose the signs to complete the number sentences.

Name _____ Date _____

Listen to the teacher. Draw your new
room. Show the furniture.

How do you know your room has 50
of empty space? Discuss.

Draw your room another way.
Show the furniture.

How do you know your room has 50
of empty space? Discuss.

Cumulative Review

Name _____ Date _____

Numbers on a Clock Lesson 1.11

Draw a line between the clocks that tell the same time.

- -

What Numbers Come Before and After? Lesson 2.3

Fill in the missing numbers.

 4 1 2 3 4 [ ] 6 7

 5 7 [ ] 9 10 11 [ ] 13

 6 6 7 8 [ ] 10 11 12

 7 14 [ ] 16 17 18 [ ] 20

Cumulative Review

Function Machines I **Lesson 5.9**

Fill in the missing number and the missing rule.

8

in	out
1	2
4	5
6	7
3	

The rule is _____

9

in	out
4	6
3	5
2	
0	2

The rule is _____

10

in	out
6	4
7	5
3	
2	0

The rule is _____

Adding and Subtracting to **100** **Lesson 8.8**

Think how many tens? Then add.

11 50 + 20 = _____

12 30 + 30 = _____

13 60 + 10 = _____

14 40 + 40 = _____

Ordinal Numbers **Lesson 8.1**

Color the correct picture.

15 The sixth mug

16 The fourth pencil

Name _____ Date _____

Lesson 8.1 **Color** the correct picture.

1 The second square

2 The tenth triangle

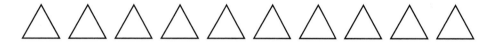

3 The fifth pentagon

Lesson 8.2 **How** many fingers?

4

5

Lesson 8.3 **How** many cents?

6

 _____ ¢

7

 _____ ¢

Lessons 8.5–8.6 **Add** or subtract. Use sticks.

8 $28 + 4 =$ _____   **9** $32 - 3 =$ _____

Lesson 8.6 **How** many sticks altogether?

10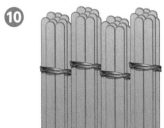

_____

11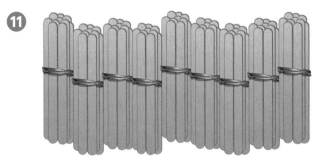

_____

Lessons 8.7–8.8 **Add** or subtract.

12 $60 + 10 =$ _____   **13** $90 - 30 =$ _____

14 $40 - 20 =$ _____   **15** $40 + 40 =$ _____

Real Math • Chapter 8

Name _____ Date _____

Put an X on the correct picture.

1 the seventh rectangle

2 the fifth circle

3 the tenth square

Fill in the missing number. Write the rule.

4

in	out
20	40
30	50
10	30
70	

The rule is _____

5

in	out
24	14
96	86
18	8
44	

The rule is _____

6

in	out
18	23
44	49
89	94
68	

The rule is _____

Ring the missing number.

7 $2 + \underline{\quad} = 11$

    a. 9   **b.** 11
    c. 2   **d.** 5

8 $7 + \underline{\quad} = 13$

    a. 7   **b.** 12
    c. 9   **d.** 6

9 $9 + \underline{\quad} = 16$

    a. 9   **b.** 10
    c. 7   **d.** 8

10 $5 + \underline{\quad} = 11$

    a. 5   **b.** 6
    c. 7   **d.** 8

Subtract. Ring the correct answer.

11 $16 - 9 = \underline{\quad}$

    a. 5   **b.** 6
    c. 7   **d.** 8

12 $13 - 6 = \underline{\quad}$

    a. 7   **b.** 8
    c. 9   **d.** 6

13 $14 - 9 = \underline{\quad}$

    a. 2   **b.** 3
    c. 4   **d.** 5

14 $10 - 6 = \underline{\quad}$

    a. 3   **b.** 4
    c. 5   **d.** 6

15 $19 - 6 = \underline{\quad}$

    a. 11   **b.** 12
    c. 13   **d.** 14

16 $11 - 4 = \underline{\quad}$

    a. 7   **b.** 8
    c. 9   **d.** 6

Name _____ Date _____

Add or subtract. Ring the correct answer.

17
$$\begin{array}{r} 39 \\ -\ 10 \\ \hline \end{array}$$
a. 49
b. 20
c. 29
d. 30

18
$$\begin{array}{r} 62 \\ +\ 20 \\ \hline \end{array}$$
a. 82
b. 42
c. 80
d. 22

19
$$\begin{array}{r} 46 \\ +\ 10 \\ \hline \end{array}$$
a. 46
b. 56
c. 66
d. 76

20
$$\begin{array}{r} 55 \\ -\ 30 \\ \hline \end{array}$$
a. 45
b. 35
c. 65
d. 25

Ring the number sentence that solves the problem.

21 Vince is 68 years old. Dave is 5 years older than Vince. How old is Dave? _____

a. $68 + 5 = 73$
b. $68 - 5 = 63$
c. $68 + 15 = 83$
d. $68 - 15 = 53$

22 Camille has 15 marbles. Mia has 10 fewer marbles than Camille has. How many marbles does Mia have? _____

a. $15 + 10 = 25$
b. $15 + 15 = 30$
c. $10 + 15 = 25$
d. $15 - 10 = 5$

23 There are 20 pairs of shoes on a shelf in a closet. How many shoes are on the shelf? _____

a. $20 + 0 = 20$
b. $20 - 10 = 10$
c. $20 + 20 = 40$
d. $20 + 10 = 30$

e Textbook This lesson is available in the *eTextbook*.

Extended Response **Draw** coins or sticks to show addition.
Make tens if you can.

24 33 + 37 = _____

25 14 + 26 = _____

Extended Response **Draw** coins or sticks to show subtraction.

26 33 − 11 = _____

27 You have 50¢. Use coins to subtract 26¢.
Show how you do this.

Thinking Story

Mr. Mudancia Changes Houses

Decorate the Engs' living room any way you wish.

 Note to Home Students listen to the Thinking Story "Mr. Mudancia Changes Houses" and answer questions about the story.

Count by tens to connect the dots.

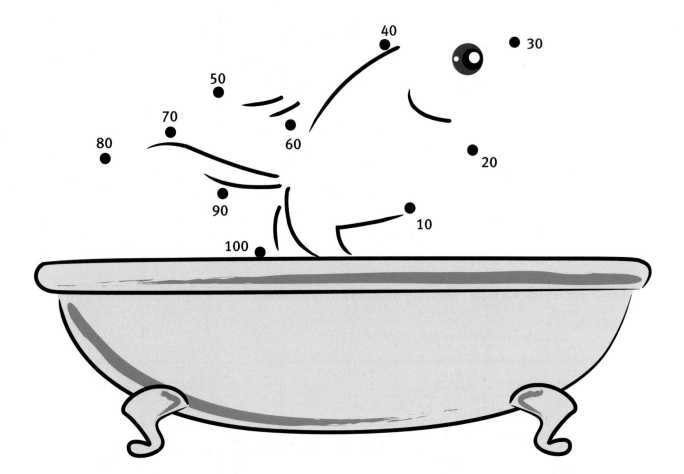

In This Chapter You Will Learn

- about polygons.
- what symmetry is.
- about paper folding.

Name _____ Date _____

Draw your necklace.

Describe your pattern.

 How do you know your necklace cost 55¢? _____

LESSON 9.1 Polygons 1

Color the figures with 3 sides blue.
Color the figures with 4 sides red.
Color the figures with 5 sides green.
Color the figures with 6 sides orange.

Draw a ring around the figures that have
sides that are the same length.

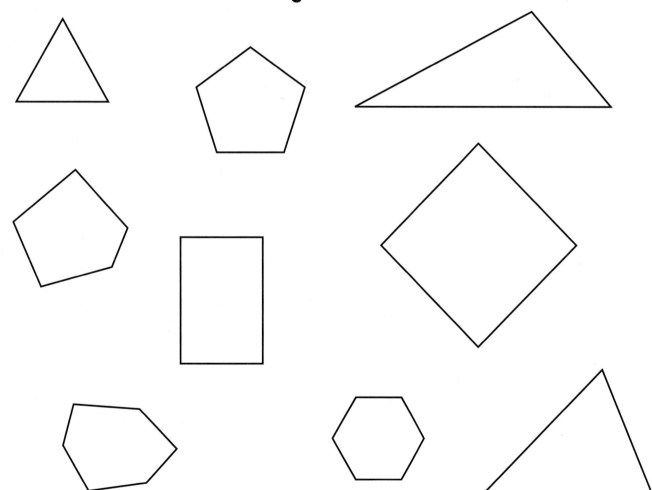

 Note to Home Students identify polygons that have equal sides.

e Textbook This lesson is available in the **eTextbook**.

Color the figures with 3 sides blue.
Color the figures with 4 sides red.
Color the figures with 5 sides green.
Color the figures with 6 sides orange.

Draw a ring around the figures that have sides that are the same length.

LESSON 9.2 Polygons II

1 **Draw** a ring around each of the closed figures.

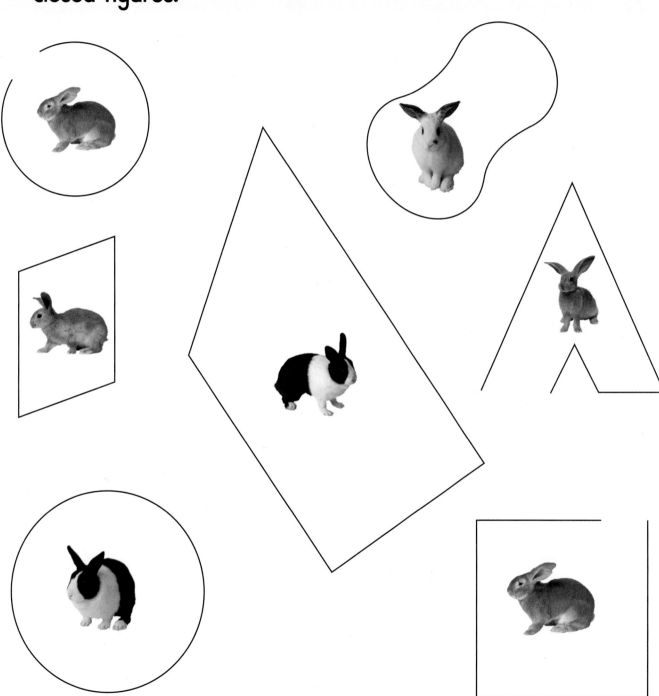

 Note to Home Students identify open and closed figures.

e Textbook This lesson is available in the *eTextbook*.

Draw one line in each figure to make two triangles. Color one triangle red. Color the other triangle any color you want.

 2

 3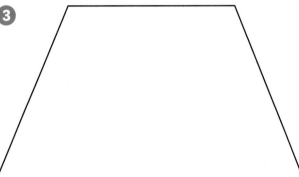

 4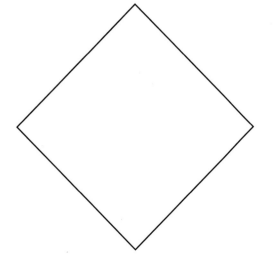

 5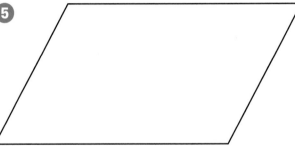

Note to Home Students divide four-sided figures into two triangles.

LESSON 9.3 Tiling with Pattern Blocks

Use pattern blocks to fill in the shapes.
Use the blocks shown.

1

2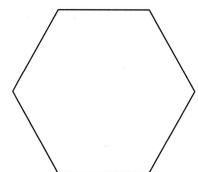

3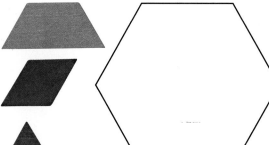

4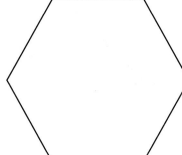

5

6

Note to Home Students fill in shapes with the given pattern blocks.

Textbook This lesson is available in the *eTextbook*.

317

Use pattern blocks to fill in the shapes.
Use the blocks shown.

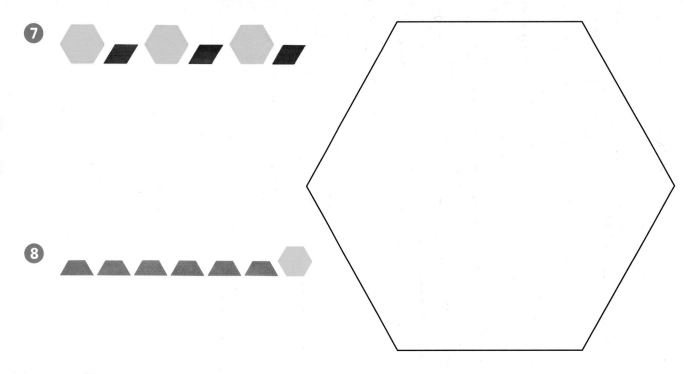

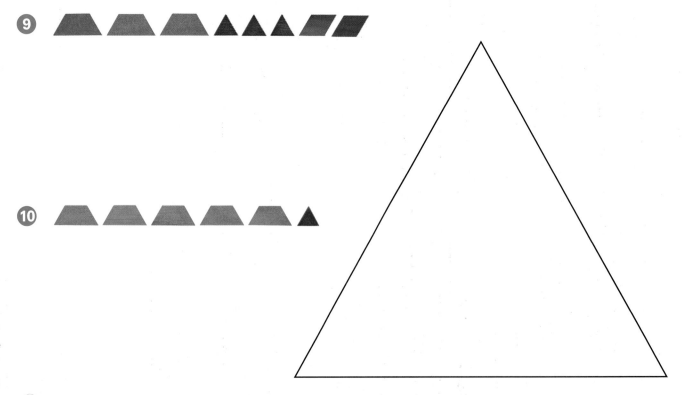

🎒 **Note to Home** Students fill in shapes with the given pattern blocks.

LESSON 9.4 **Symmetry I**

Draw each line of symmetry. Use your mirror to help.

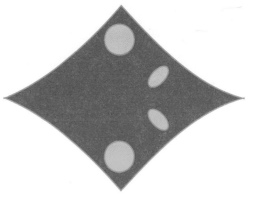

🔒 **Note to Home** Students use mirrors to find lines of symmetry.

📱 **eTextbook** This lesson is available in the *eTextbook*.

319

Draw each line of symmetry. Use a mirror to help.

🎒 **Note to Home** Students use mirrors to find lines of symmetry.

320

Real Math • Chapter 9 • Lesson 4

Name _____ Date _____

Draw a second triangle to form a four-sided figure. Make the figure symmetrical. The first one is done for you.

1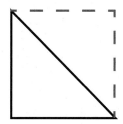

2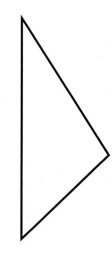

3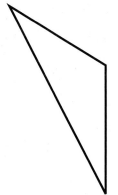

4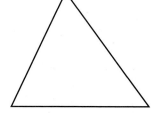

Note to Home Students draw a second triangle to make a symmetrical four-sided figure.

Textbook This lesson is available in the *eTextbook*.

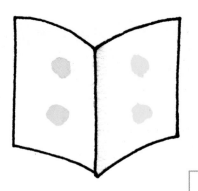

5 How many? ▢

Now how many? ▢

$2 + 2 =$ _____

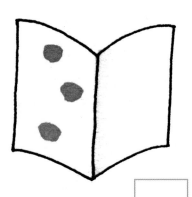

6 How many? ▢

Now how many? ▢

$3 + 3 =$ _____

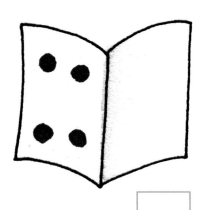

7 How many? ▢

Now how many? ▢

$4 + 4 =$ _____

🎒 **Note to Home** Students explore relationships between symmetry and doubles.

Name _____ Date _____

Listen to the teacher.

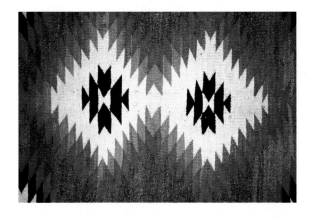

What shapes can you find?

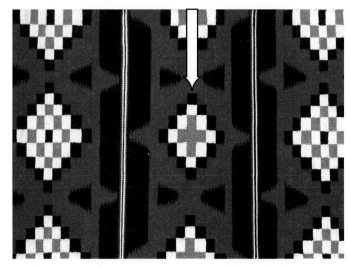

Use blocks to make this figure.

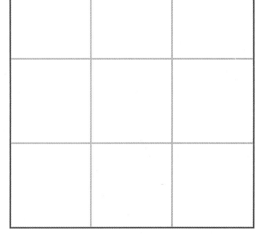

 Show how you did it.

How many squares ~~esign?~~

💡 **Jane will Make a List.**

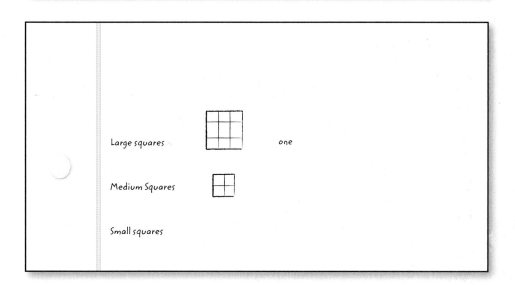

💡 **Show how you solved the problem.**

There are _____ squares in the design.

Cumulative Review

Name _____ Date _____

Counting by Tens Lesson 8.6

There are 10 sticks in a bundle.

How many sticks altogether?

1   _____

2  _____

3  _____

4  _____

5  _____

6  _____

Missing Addends II Lesson 7.2

Write how many were added to the can.

7  $+ \boxed{} = 8$

8  $+ \boxed{} = 6$

Cumulative Review

Adding and Subtracting (Vertical Form) **Lesson 4.7**

Solve these problems.

9
$$\begin{array}{r} 8 \\ + 2 \\ \hline \end{array}$$

10
$$\begin{array}{r} 6 \\ - 1 \\ \hline \end{array}$$

11
$$\begin{array}{r} 1 \\ + 3 \\ \hline \end{array}$$

12
$$\begin{array}{r} 3 \\ + 1 \\ \hline \end{array}$$

Mental Subtraction **Lesson 5.8**

Do these in your head. Then write the answers.

13 $6 + 2 = $ _____

14 $6 + 1 = $ _____

15 $4 - 0 = $ _____

16 $4 - 1 = $ _____

Polygons I **Lesson 9.1**

Color the shapes with 3 sides blue. Color the shapes with 4 sides red. Color the shapes with 5 sides green. Draw rings around the shapes that have sides that are the same length.

17

18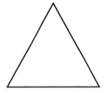

19

20

21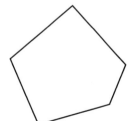

22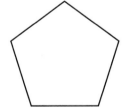

Real Math • Chapter 9

LESSON 9.6 Congruent Figures

Make an X on the shape that is congruent. Trace to check. Then color the congruent shapes the same color.

1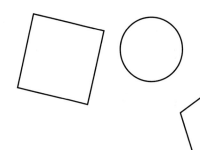

2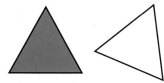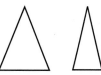

3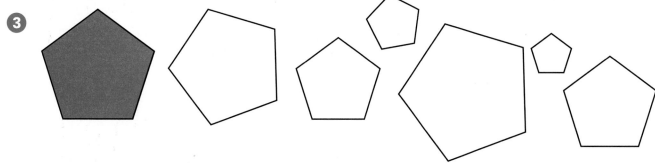

🔖 **Note to Home** Students identify congruent shapes.

💻 **Textbook** This lesson is available in the *eTextbook*.

Trace to find shapes that are congruent to this triangle. Then color all of the congruent triangles the same color.

Name _____ Date _____

Listen to the story. Draw a line to show where Roger walked.

🍼 **Note to Home** Students are introduced to a map described in a story.

📱 **Textbook** This lesson is available in the *eTextbook*.

Tom starts at home and walks along the path shown to Ann's house.

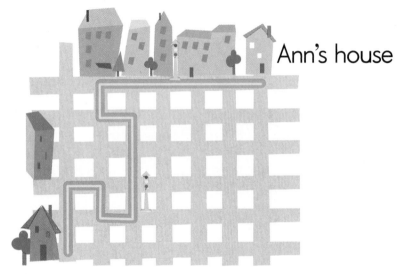

Ann's house

Tom's house

1 How many blocks did Tom walk? _____

2 Could Tom come home by walking fewer blocks? _____

3 What is the shortest number of blocks he could walk to get home? _____

4 Draw one of the shortest paths between Ann's house and Tom's house.

Note to Home Students read and interpret a map.

LESSON 9.8 Space Figures

Listen to the story.

1

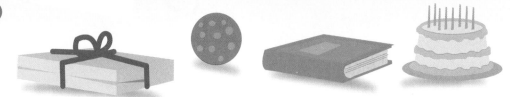

2

3

Note to Home Students estimate which of the objects will fit in the given box.

eTextbook This lesson is available in the *eTextbook*.

Ring objects with the same shape.

 Note to Home Students identify space figures.

Name _____ Date _____

Construct a cube in class. Then examine your cube and your *Number Cubes.* Answer the questions.

This is a face.

1 How many faces does each cube have?

_____

This is an edge.

2 How many edges does each cube have?

_____

This is a corner.

3 How many corners does each cube have? _____

🎒 **Note to Home** Students study the properties of a cube.

📖 **Textbook** This lesson is available in the *eTextbook.*

Copyright © SRA/McGraw-Hill.

Color the shapes this way.

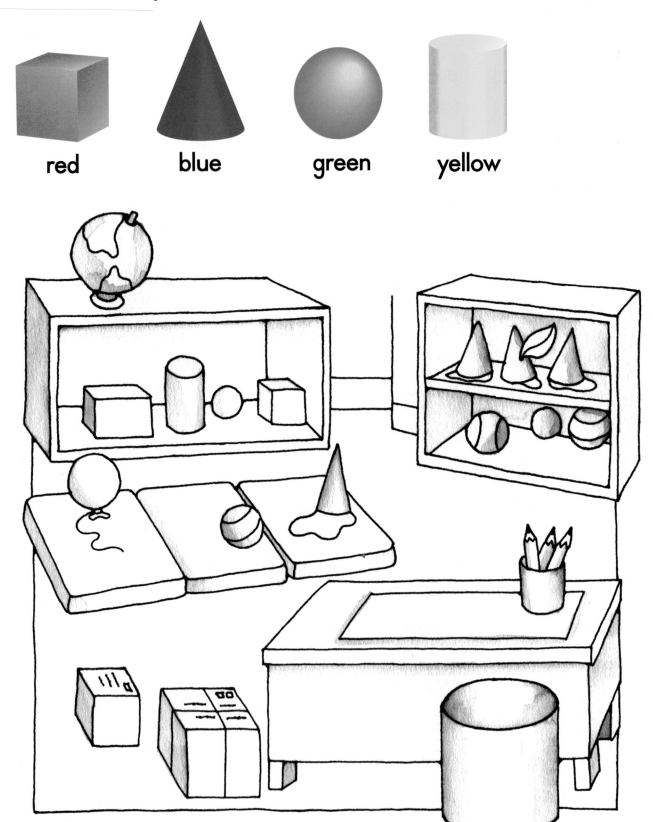

red   blue   green   yellow

🎒 **Note to Home** Students identify space figures.

LESSON 9.10

More Paper Folding

Making a Tetrahedron

1. Use the pattern your teacher gives you. Cut out the pattern on the solid lines.

2. Fold on the dotted lines.

3. Glue the triangle with a solid 1 on it over the triangle with the dotted 1.

4. Glue the triangle with a solid 2 on it over the triangle with the dotted 2.

5. Finally, glue the triangle with a solid 3 on it over the triangle with the dotted 3.

Note to Home Students create a tetrahedron.

eTextbook This lesson is available in the *eTextbook*.

Examine your cube and your tetrahedron. Answer the questions.

6 How many faces does the cube have?

_____

7 What shape are those faces? _____

8 How many faces does the tetrahedron have? _____

9 What shape are those faces? _____

Now try putting the tetrahedron inside the cube. Try different ways. Then look at the picture.

10 Is this the way you put your tetrahedron inside the cube? _____

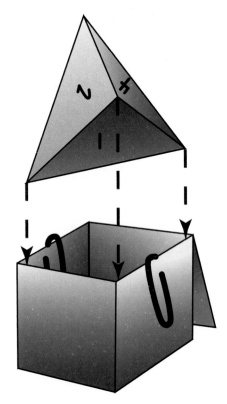

 Note to Home Students study a cube and a tetrahedron.

Real Math • Chapter 9 • Lesson 10

Name _____ Date _____

Make a design with no holes.
Use these tiles.

Draw your design.

Describe your pattern.

_____

How do you know your design costs
95¢? _____

Draw another design.

Describe your pattern.

_____

How do you know your design
costs 95¢? _____

Cumulative Review

Name _____ Date _____

1 Draw a ring around the longest object.
Place an X on the shortest object.

· ·

$1 and $5 Bills Lesson 5.2

Draw bills to make the correct amount.
Use as few bills as possible.

2

3

Cumulative Review

Missing Addends II Lesson7.2

Write how many were added to the can.

④ 6 + ☐ = 8

⑤ 5 + ☐ = 6

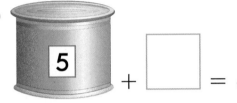

- -

Missing Addends II Lesson 7.2

Listen. Then find the missing number.

⑥ Sonya has $6. She wants to buy a book that costs $10. How much more money does Sonya need?

$$6 + \boxed{} = 10$$

⑦ Juan wants to read 8 books. So far he has read 5 books. How many more books will Juan read?

$$5 + \boxed{} = 8$$

- -

Symmetry II Lesson 9.5

Draw a second triangle to form a four-sided figure. Make the figure symmetrical.

⑧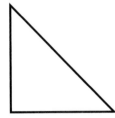

⑨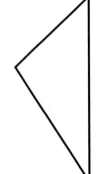

Name _____ Date _____

Lesson 9.1 **Follow** the directions.

Color the shape with 3 sides blue.

Color the shape with 4 sides red.

Color the shape with 5 sides green.

Color the shape with 6 sides orange.

1 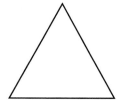 **2**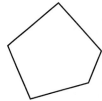

3  **4**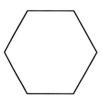

Lesson 9.2 **Draw** one line in each figure to make two triangles. Color one of the triangles red.

5   **6**  **7**

Lesson 9.6 Put an X on the figure that is congruent. Trace to check.

8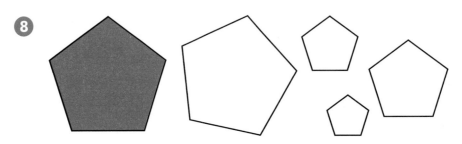

Lesson 9.8 Ring objects with the same figure.

9

10

Lessons 9.9–9.10 Fill in the answers.

11 How many faces does a cube have? _____

12 What shape are those faces? _____

13 How many faces does a tetrahedron have?

_____

Name _____ Date _____

Read and color.

1 Color the shapes with 4 sides blue.

2 Color the shapes with 3 sides yellow.

3 Color the shapes with 5 sides red.

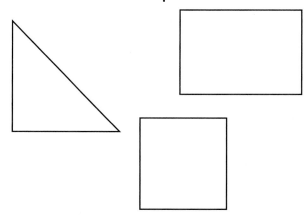
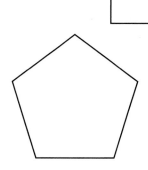
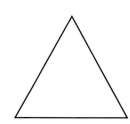

4 Ring the shapes that have sides that are the same length.

Draw a line to make both parts the same.

5

6

Practice Test

How many tally marks?

7 |||| |||| |||| |||| ||||

    a. 25   **b.** 15
    c. 4   **d.** 20

8 |||| |||| |||| |||| ||||

    a. 24   **b.** 9
    c. 5   **d.** 30

9 |||| |||| |||| |||| |||| |||| |||| |||| |||| |||| ||

    a. 11   **b.** 50   **c.** 52   **d.** 55

Ring >, <, or =.

10 $16 - 9 \bigcirc 8$

    a. >
    b. <
    c. =
    d. Not here

11 $14 - 8 \bigcirc 6$

    a. >
    b. <
    c. =
    d. Not here

12 $52 + 8 \bigcirc 55$

    a. >
    b. <
    c. =
    d. Not here

13 $25 + 10 \bigcirc 35$

    a. >
    b. <
    c. =
    d. Not here

Name _____ Date _____

Ring the congruent shape.

14

a.   b.

c.   d.

15

a.   b.

c.   d.

Ring the same shape.

16

a.   b.

c.   d.

17

a.   b.

c.   d.

18 **Extended Response** Circle the shapes that will fold to make a cube. Explain your answer.

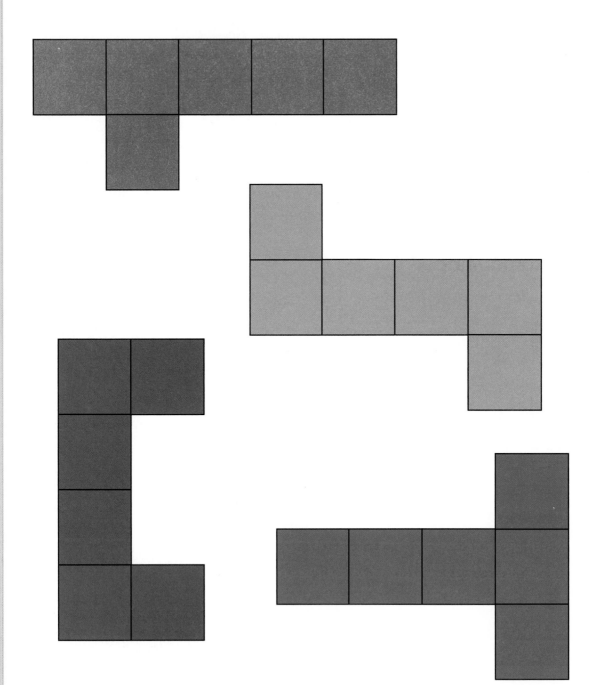

Thinking Story

How Ms. Eng
Doubled
Her Money

Match the money with the doubled amount.

 Note to Home Students listen to the Thinking Story "How Ms. Eng Doubled Her Money" and answer questions about the story.

e Textbook This lesson is available in the *eTextbook*.

Find the words that go with the number 2, and ring them.

```
S   I   N   G   L   E
P   A   I   R   N   O
L   L   T   W   O   N
D   O   U   B   L   E
B   N   O   U   E   B
L   E   G   A   N   P
```

Word List:

two

pair

double

CHAPTER 10 Fractions

In This Chapter You Will Learn

- about halves, thirds, and fourths.
- more about clocks and telling time.

Name _____ Date _____

Listen to the problem.

Show how you made two equal portions. _____

How do you know the two portions are equal?

· ·

_____

_____

LESSON 10.1

Dividing Sets into Halves

For each set, draw a line to divide the set into halves. Make sure each set has the same number of objects. Then write the number.

1

Half of 4 is _____ .

2

Half of 10 is _____ .

3

Half of 8 is _____ .

4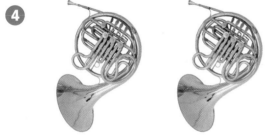

Half of 2 is _____ .

5

Half of 6 is _____ .

 Note to Home Students divide sets of objects into two sets of equal numbers.

e Textbook This lesson is available in the **eTextbook**.

These pictures show only half of a set. Draw the other half to show how many would be in the whole group.

6
Half of _____ is 2.

7
Half of _____ is 3.

8
Half of _____ is 4.

Count the dots. Write the number. Ring the set if it can be divided into two equal sets.

9

10

11

12

Note to Home Students show understanding that dividing a set of objects into halves creates two sets of the same number of objects.

LESSON
10.2 **Estimating Halves**

Listen to the problems.

1 This jug was full of juice. Then Lisa and her friends drank half of the juice. Draw a line to show how much juice will be left.

2 Terrel is making orange juice. So far he has squeezed half of the oranges. Draw a line on the jar to show how full the jar will be when he has squeezed all of the oranges.

3 ▶ Extended Response ▶ Holly wanted to pour half of the juice to share with her sister. Did she? Explain.

_____

_____

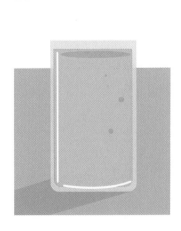

🎒 **Note to Home** Students estimate half of a given amount.

Listen to the problems.

4

Scott is walking home. He has walked half of the way. Draw the rest of the path.

5 There are two paths to the lake. Draw an X on each path to show half of the way.

6

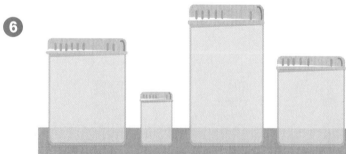

Draw a line to show where you would fill each jar if you were filling it halfway.

 Note to Home Students solve word problems.

LESSON 10.3 Introducing Fourths and Halves of Numbers

Write the missing fractions on the strips.

1

$\frac{1}{2}$	

$\frac{1}{4}$			

Write the answers.

1 $\frac{1}{2}$ of 10 is _____

2 $\frac{1}{2}$ of 8 is _____

3 $\frac{1}{2}$ of 12 is _____

4 $\frac{1}{2}$ of 6 is _____

5 $\frac{1}{2}$ of 2 is _____

6 $\frac{1}{2}$ of 16 is _____

Note to Home Students identify fractions and identify halves of numbers.

e Textbook This lesson is available in the *eTextbook*.

Listen to the problems.

7 There are 8 houses on Raulito's street. Of the 8 houses, $\frac{1}{2}$ of the houses are painted brown. How many houses are brown? _____

8 SOCIAL STUDIES Raulito's school is 6 blocks from his house. The library is $\frac{1}{2}$ that distance from his house. How many blocks is the library from Raulito's house? _____

9 Extended Response Draw a map to show what you know about Raulito's street.

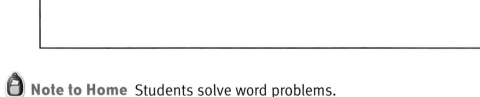
Copyright © SRA/McGraw-Hill.

LESSON 10.4

Introducing Thirds and Fractions of Length

1 The bench is 4 feet long. Mark an X on the bench 1 foot from the end.

2 The front post is 2 meters high. Draw a bug on the post 1 meter from the top.

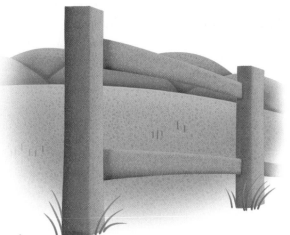

3 The road is 3 miles long. Misha has walked 1 mile. Mark an X to show where Misha is.

 Note to Home Students identify fractions of length.

e Textbook This lesson is available in the *eTextbook*.

Ring the correct answer.

4

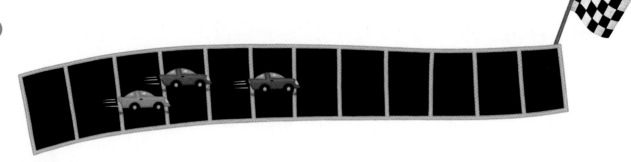

The green car is $\frac{1}{2}$ $\frac{1}{3}$ $\frac{1}{4}$ of the way to the finish line.

The red car is $\frac{1}{2}$ $\frac{1}{3}$ $\frac{1}{4}$ of the way to the finish line.

The blue car is $\frac{1}{2}$ $\frac{1}{3}$ $\frac{1}{4}$ of the way to the finish line.

5

Elan is swimming across the pool.

He is $\frac{1}{2}$ $\frac{1}{3}$ $\frac{1}{4}$ of the way to the ladder.

Note to Home Students identify fractions of length.

Exploring Problem Solving

Name _____ Date _____

Listen to the problem.

💡 **Januah will Act It Out with Objects and Draw Pictures to solve the problem.**

1  **2**  **3**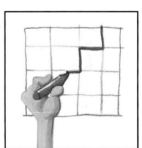

4 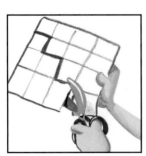 **5**

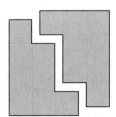

Are the two Yuzzles the same size? _____

Are they the same shape? _____

Draw and color as many different Yuzzles as you can.

Use a different color for each different shape.

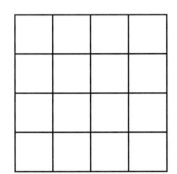 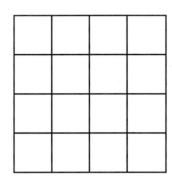

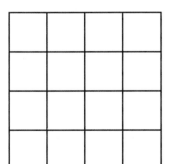 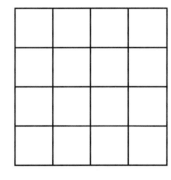

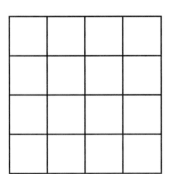 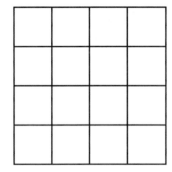

How do you know all the Yuzzles are the same size?

_____

Cumulative Review

Name _____ Date _____

Number Lines Lesson 2.1

Write how many.

1 [　]

2 [　]

3 [　]

4  [　]

....

Using a Number Line Lesson 4.8

Listen. Then circle the number you land on.

5

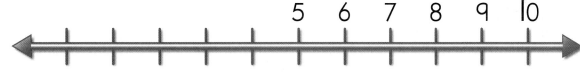

                     5 6 7 8 9 10

Start at 5. Hop on 1, and then circle the number you land on.

6

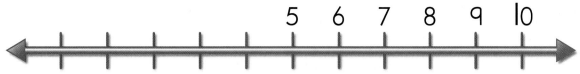

                     5 6 7 8 9 10

Start at 6. Hop on 2, and then circle the number you land on.

Cumulative Review

Money to 4̶0 Cents **Lesson 8.3**

How many cents?

7 _____ ¢

8 _____ ¢

9 _____ ¢

10 _____ ¢

11 _____ ¢

Space Figures **Lesson 9.8**

Circle the object that will fit in the box.

12

13

LESSON 10.5 **More Fractions of Length**

Ring the correct answer.

1 about $\frac{1}{2}$ $\frac{1}{4}$ as long

2 about $\frac{1}{2}$ $\frac{1}{3}$ as long

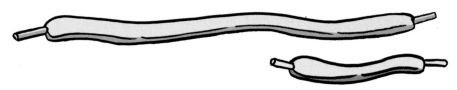

3 about $\frac{1}{2}$ $\frac{1}{4}$ as long

4 about $\frac{1}{2}$ $\frac{1}{3}$ as long

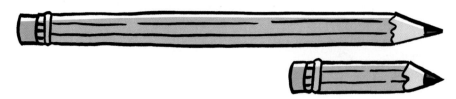

Copyright © SRA/McGraw-Hill.

Note to Home Students identify fractions of length.

eTextbook This lesson is available in the **eTextbook**.

Follow the directions.

5 Draw a rope that is $\frac{1}{2}$ as long.

6 Draw what this jug would look like if it were filled about $\frac{1}{3}$ full.

7 Draw a picture of anything you like. Then draw the same object that is $\frac{1}{4}$, $\frac{1}{3}$, or $\frac{1}{2}$ as long. Write the fraction under the picture.

 Play the **Diviso Game.**

 Note to Home Students identify fractions of length.

LESSON 10.6

Multiples of Length

Listen to the problems.

1 This is how far Chen gets with 1 giant step. Make an X to show how far she will get with 3 giant steps.

start

2 A big turtle and a little turtle started crawling away from the rock at the same time. You can see how far the little turtle has crawled. The big turtle crawls twice as fast. Draw a picture to show where the big turtle would be.

3 This is Pinocchio. When he tells a lie, his nose becomes 4 times as long. Finish the second picture to show how long his nose is when he tells a lie.

Note to Home Students identify multiples of length.

e Textbook This lesson is available in the *eTextbook*.

Listen to the problems. Follow the directions.

4 Make a bone 3 times as long as this.

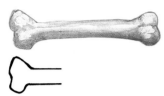

5 Make a bone 2 times as long as this.

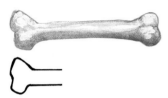

6 Make a bone 4 times as long as this.

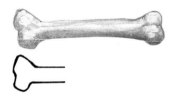

7 Eva and Connor each have a plant. Connor's plant is 2 times as tall as Eva's. Draw Connor's plant.

🎒 **Note to Home** Students identify multiples of length.

LESSON 10.7 **Fractional Parts**

Ring the fraction that relates
to the picture.

1 $\dfrac{1}{2}$ $\dfrac{1}{3}$ $\dfrac{1}{4}$

2 $\dfrac{1}{2}$ $\dfrac{1}{3}$ $\dfrac{1}{4}$

3 $\dfrac{1}{2}$ $\dfrac{1}{3}$ $\dfrac{1}{4}$

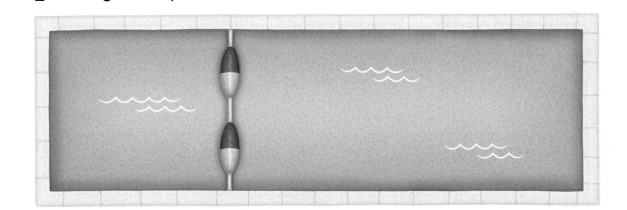

4 $\dfrac{1}{2}$ $\dfrac{1}{3}$ $\dfrac{1}{4}$

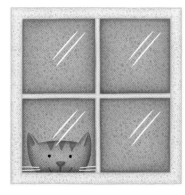

Copyright © SRA/McGraw-Hill.

Note to Home Students identify fractions of figures.

eTextbook This lesson is available in the *eTextbook*.

Follow **the directions.**

5 Julie's parents are painting one wall of her room orange. They have finished painting $\frac{1}{3}$ of the wall so far. Show how much of the wall has been painted orange.

6 Reese has a square backyard. His mother planted flowers in $\frac{1}{2}$ of the yard. Show how much of the yard has flowers planted.

7 Color half of each of these shapes.

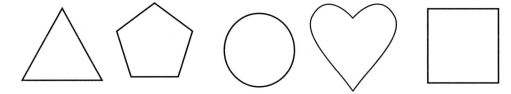

8 **Extended Response** Color $\frac{1}{2}$ of each large rectangle. Do it 6 different ways.

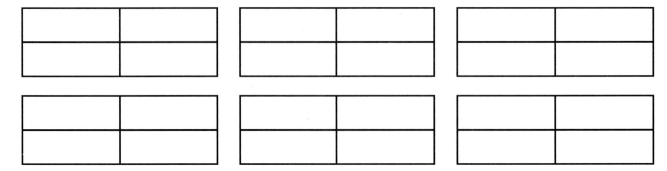

🎒 Note to Home Students identify fractions of shapes.

LESSON 10.8

Fractions on a Clock

Follow the directions for each problem.

1 What time is it? _____
What time will it be half an hour later? _____
Show what the clock will look like at that time.

2 What time is it? _____
What time will it be an hour later? _____
Show what the clock will look like at that time.

3 What time is it? _____
What time will it be half an hour later? _____
Show what the clock will look like at that time.

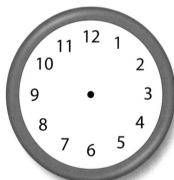

4 What time is it? _____
What time will it be an hour later? _____
Show what the clock will look like at that time.

Note to Home Students review telling time to the hour and half hour.

Textbook This lesson is available in the *eTextbook.*

Follow the directions for each problem.

5 Color $\frac{1}{2}$. Do it two ways.

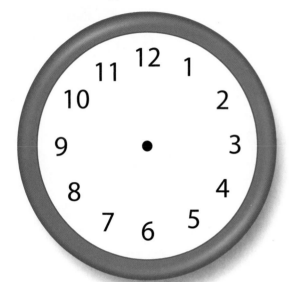

6 Color $\frac{1}{4}$. Do it two ways.

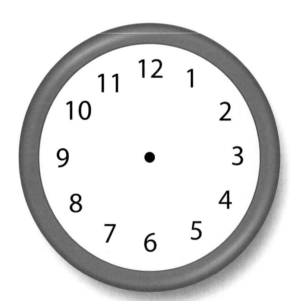

Note to Home Students review halves of shapes.

Name _____ Date _____

Fractions and Multiples of Time

Listen to the problems.
Write the answers.

1 It takes Jon about 5 minutes to peel
1 potato. About how long would it
take Jon to peel 2 potatoes?
about _____ minutes

2 **REAL WORLD** It took Stacia about 1 minute to
run $\frac{1}{2}$ of the track. About how long
would it take her to run the entire
track? about _____ minutes

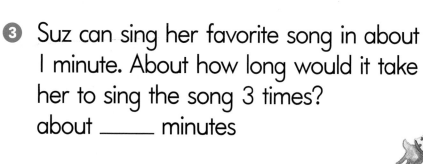

3 Suz can sing her favorite song in about
1 minute. About how long would it take
her to sing the song 3 times?
about _____ minutes

🎒 **Note to Home** Students estimate fractions and multiples of time.

📱 **Textbook** This lesson is available in the *eTextbook*.

Listen to the problems.
Write the answers.

4 Malik painted 2 pictures. It took him about 1 hour. About how long would it take him to paint 1 picture?

about _____ hour

5 Yesterday Andi practiced for $\frac{1}{2}$ hour. Today she will practice twice as long. How long will she practice today?

_____ hour

6 On Saturday Luis and his grandmother spent 1 hour at the park. Today they stayed at the park twice as long. They arrived at 2:00. What time was it when they left? _____

Copyright © SRA/McGraw-Hill.

🎒 **Note to Home** Students estimate fractions and multiples of time.

Name _____ Date _____

Listen to the problem.

Draw your solutions on these figures.

How did you solve the problem? _____

_____

Draw any shape and then show how
many Yuzzles would fit into it.

Cumulative Review

Name _____ Date _____

What Number Comes Next? Lesson 2.2

Draw one more. Then write how many.

1   ____

2  ____

3

 ____

4   ____

Adding 5 Lesson 5.4

Write the number sentences.

5 $5 + \boxed{} = 9$

6 $5 + \boxed{} = \boxed{}$

7 $5 + \boxed{} = \boxed{}$

8 $5 + \boxed{} = \boxed{}$

Cumulative Review

Adding 10 and Adding 9 Lesson 6.3

Solve.

9 7 + 10 = _____

10 7 + 9 = _____

11 5 + 5 = _____

12 5 + 6 = _____

13 7 + 7 = _____

14 8 + 7 = _____

....

Addition with Numbers to 40 Lesson 8.4

There are too many crayons.

Ring the correct number of crayons.

15 30

16 15

17 10

....

Introducing Fourths and Halves of Numbers Lesson 10.3

Write the answers.

18 $\frac{1}{2}$ of 10 is _____

19 $\frac{1}{2}$ of 12 is _____

20 $\frac{1}{2}$ of 2 is _____

Real Math • Chapter 10

Name _____ Date _____

Lesson 10.1 **For** each set, draw a line to divide the set into halves. Make sure each set has the same amount. Then write the number.

1

Half of 8 is _____.

2

Half of 4 is _____.

Lesson 10.2 **Listen** to the problem. Then follow the directions.

3 Tina and her friends drank half of the lemonade in the pitcher. Draw a line to show how much lemonade will be left.

Lesson 10.3 **Write** the answers.

4 $\frac{1}{2}$ of 6 is _____

5 $\frac{1}{2}$ of 18 is _____

Lesson 10.6 **Listen** to the problems. Follow the directions.

6 Make a pencil 4 times as long as this.

7 Make a pencil that is 3 times as long as this.

8 Make a pencil that is 2 times as long as this.

Lesson 10.7 **What** fraction of the pizza was eaten?

9  $\frac{1}{2}$ $\frac{1}{3}$ $\frac{1}{4}$

Name _____ Date _____

Draw an X to solve.

1 Tabitha walks $\frac{1}{2}$ of the path. Put an X where she is now.

2 Lonnie is $\frac{1}{3}$ of the way from the end of the path. Put an X where he is now.

Draw a line to solve.

3 Draw a line that is half as long.

4 Draw a line that is twice as long.

5 Draw a line that is 4 times as long.

6 Draw a line that is 3 times as long.

Ring the number sentence.

7 Zoey has 43 pieces of bubble gum. She gave 13 pieces to Jorge. How many pieces of bubble gum did Zoey have then?

a. $43 + 13 = 56$ **b.** $56 - 13 = 43$

c. $43 - 13 = 30$ **d.** $13 + 10 = 23$

8 Jordan had 35 pennies in his pocket. He put 10 more pennies in his pocket. How many pennies were in Jordan's pocket then?

a. $35 + 10 = 45$ **b.** $35 - 10 = 25$

c. $35 + 10 = 40$ **d.** $35 + 10 = 55$

Mark the figure that is congruent.

9

a.   **b.**   **c.**   **d.**

10

a.   **b.**   **c.**   **d.**

Name _____ Date _____

Ring the answer.

⑪ $\frac{1}{2}$ of 8 is

   a. 4
   b. 8
   c. 16
   d. 2

⑫ $\frac{1}{2}$ of 18 is

   a. 18
   b. 8
   c. 9
   d. 20

⑬ $\frac{1}{2}$ of 14 is

   a. 7
   b. 14
   c. 10
   c. 4

⑭ $\frac{1}{2}$ of 4 is

   a. 4
   b. 2
   c. 8
   d. 1

What fraction of the figure is colored?

⑮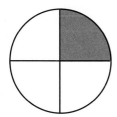

   a. $\frac{1}{2}$ **b.** $\frac{1}{4}$

   c. $\frac{1}{6}$ **d.** $\frac{1}{3}$

⑯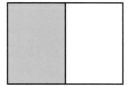

   a. $\frac{1}{4}$ **b.** $\frac{1}{3}$

   c. $\frac{1}{2}$ **d.** $\frac{1}{8}$

Draw hands to show 1 hour later.

17

18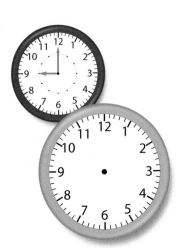

19

Draw hands to show $\frac{1}{2}$ hour later.

20

21

22

Draw hands to show 2 hours later.

23

24

25

Thinking Story

MEASURING BOWSER

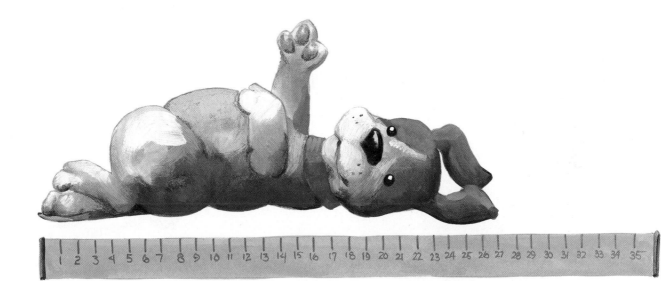

How many inches long is Bowser?
Write the number. _____

 Note to Home Students listen to the Thinking Story "Measuring Bowser" and answer questions about the story.

e Textbook This lesson is available in the *eTextbook*.

Ring the tool used to measure
Bowser's weight.

In This Chapter You Will Learn

- how to measure temperature, length, weight, and capacity.
- different units of measurement.

Name _____ Date _____

Listen to the problem.

Letter	Sample Description	Names				
A	Ice Water	0	0	0	0	0
B	Hot Water					
C						
D						
E						
F						

 Did everyone write the same number for each sample? _____

 What do you like about this way to record temperature? _____

How could you measure better? _____

Name _____ Date _____

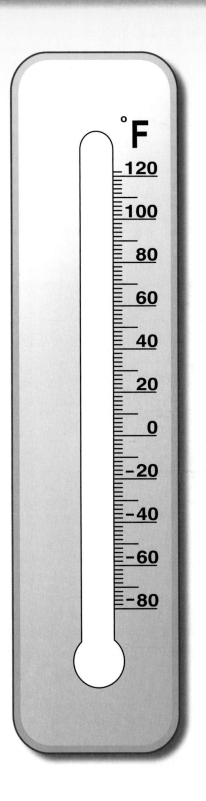

1 Draw the temperature.

2 Write the temperature. _____

🍼 Note to Home Students measure the temperature of the classroom in degrees Fahrenheit.

📱 Textbook This lesson is available in the *eTextbook*.

Outdoor Temperature Changes

3 Draw the temperature.

4 Write the temperature.

5 Write the date.

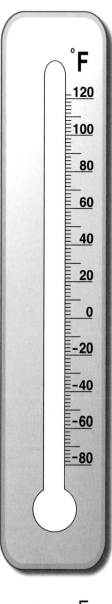

Temperature   _____ F   _____ F   _____ F

Date   _____   _____   _____

Note to Home Students measure the outdoor temperature in degrees Fahrenheit over a period of a few days.

Name _____   Date _____

Measuring Temperature in Celsius

Cold Water

1 Record the temperature every 30 minutes.

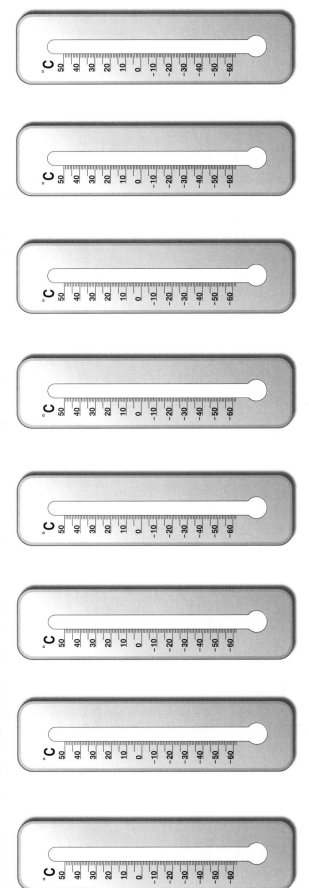

__°C	__°C	__°C	__°C	__°C	__°C	__°C	__°C
Start	30 minutes	1 hour	1 hour 30 minutes	2 hours	2 hours 30 minutes	3 hours	3 hours 30 minutes

Note to Home Students use a thermometer to measure temperature in Celsius. Students observe that the temperature of cold water that has been placed in room temperature changes over time.

ⓔ Textbook This lesson is available in the *eTextbook*.

389

Hot Water

2 Record the temperature every 30 minutes.

Start	30 minutes	1 hour	1 hour 30 minutes	2 hours	2 hours 30 minutes	3 hours	3 hours 30 minutes
___ C	___ C	___ C	___ C	___ C	___ C	___ C	___ C

Note to Home Students use a thermometer to measure temperature in Celsius. Students observe that the temperature of hot water that has been placed in room temperature changes over time.

LESSON 11.3 Measuring Length in Nonstandard Units

How tall are you?

1 What will you measure with? _____

2 How tall is your partner? _____

3 What did your partner measure with? _____

4 How tall are you? _____

Copyright © SRA/McGraw-Hill.

Note to Home Students measure and report height using various units to establish the need for standard units.

How close can you get?

Child	Estimate	Measure
⑤		
⑥		
⑦		
⑧		
⑨		

🎒 Note to Home Students estimate and then measure height using stick units.

Name _____ Date _____

How many centimeters? Use your ruler to find out.

1

2

3

4

Copyright © SRA/McGraw-Hill.

How big is a smile?

	Me	My Partner
5	_____ centimeters	_____ centimeters
6	_____ centimeters	_____ centimeters

7 Partner's name _____

8 Who has the bigger smile? _____

 Play the **Find the Distance Game.**

Note to Home Students measure length in centimeters.

Name _____ Date _____

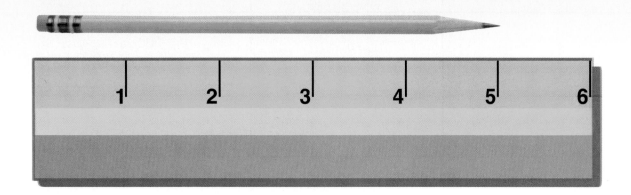

This pencil is about 5 inches long.

Measure things in your classroom.
Estimate first. Then use your ruler to check.

	Object	Estimate	Measure
1			_____ inches
2			_____ inches
3			_____ inches

 Note to Home Students estimate and measure in inches.

e Textbook This lesson is available in the *eTextbook*.

Estimate first. Then use your ruler to check.

	Object	Estimate	Measure
4			_____ inches
5			_____ inches
6			_____ inches
7			_____ inches
8			_____ inches

Copyright © SRA/McGraw-Hill.

Note to Home Students estimate and measure in inches.

Name _____   Date _____

Listen to the problem.

5 centimeters

How many cubes do you need? _____

Marcus will Write a Number Sentence to solve the problem.

Will Marcus get the
correct answer to
the problem? _____

5+5+5+5 = ___

How would you solve the problem?

_____

Mi Lei will Draw a Picture to solve the problem.

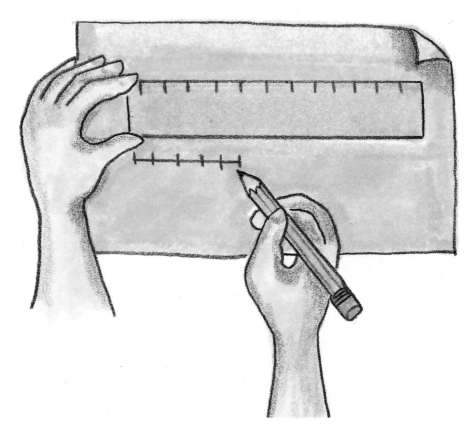

Write your solution to the problem.

_____

How did you solve it? _____

_____

Cumulative Review

Name _____ Date _____

Measuring Length in Centimeters Lesson 11.4

How many centimeters? Use your ruler to find out.

1

2

3

4

....

Fractions and Multiples of Time Lesson 10.9

Listen to the problems. Write the answers.

5 It takes Jon about 5 minutes to peel 1 potato. About how long would it take Jon to peel 2 potatoes?

about _____ minutes

6 Malik painted 2 pictures. It took him about 1 hour. About how long would it take him to paint 1 picture?

about _____ hour

Cumulative Review

Adding and Subtracting on a Number Line Lesson 4.9

Solve these problems. Use the number line.

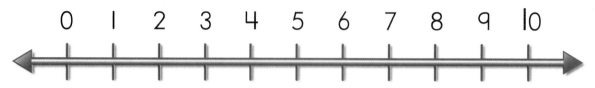

0 1 2 3 4 5 6 7 8 9 10

7 $4 + 2 =$ _____   **8** $7 + 1 =$ _____

9 $5 - 1 =$ _____   **10** $8 - 3 =$ _____

11 $3 + 2 =$ _____   **12** $3 + 3 =$ _____

Counting by Tens Lesson 8.6

How many tally marks? Ring sets of ten to help you count.

13 ||||| ||||| ||||| ||||| ||||| ||||| ||||| ||||| ||||| ||||| ||||| ||||| _____

14 ||||| ||||| ||||| ||||| ||||| ||||| ||||| ||||| ||||| ||||| _____

Numbers on a Clock Lesson 1.11

What time is it?

15

16

Real Math • Chapter 11

Name _____ Date _____

 LESSON 11.6 **Measuring Weight in Grams**

How many grams?

1

_____ grams

2

_____ grams

3

_____ grams

Copyright © SRA/McGraw-Hill.

How much do the objects weigh altogether?

4 Estimate.   _____ grams

5 Then weigh.   _____ grams

 Note to Home Students estimate weight in grams.

Textbook This lesson is available in the **eTextbook**.

A bar of soap weighs about 100 grams.

6 Ring the objects that weigh less than 100 grams.

7 Ring the objects that weigh more than 100 grams.

 Note to Home Students estimate and measure weight in grams.

Name _____ Date _____

Measuring Weight in Pounds

① How much does each block weigh? _____

② How much does each book weigh? _____

Note to Home Students measure weight in pounds.

eTextbook This lesson is available in the *eTextbook*.

I pound   5 pounds   20 pounds

3 Ring the objects that weigh less than 5 pounds.

Extended Response Tell how you know.

_____

4 Ring the objects that weigh more than 20 pounds.

Extended Response Tell how you know.

_____

🎒 **Note to Home** Students estimate weight in pounds.

Name _____ Date _____

Measuring Capacity in Liters

This container holds 1 liter.

Estimate how much each container holds. Then measure.

	Container	Estimate	Measure
1		less than a liter more than a liter	less than a liter more than a liter
2		less than a liter more than a liter	less than a liter more than a liter
3		less than a liter more than a liter	less than a liter more than a liter
4		less than a liter more than a liter	less than a liter more than a liter

Copyright © SRA/McGraw-Hill.

Note to Home Students estimate and measure capacity in liters.

Textbook This lesson is available in the *eTextbook*.

Ring the container that holds more.

5

6

7

8 ⟩Extended Response⟩ Anna and her mother are going to make tie-dyed shirts. They need to fill the bucket with 6 liters of water to mix the dye. How can they use a 2-liter bottle to measure the correct amount of water? Explain how you know.

Copyright © SRA/McGraw-Hill.

🎒 **Note to Home** Students estimate capacity.

Name _____ Date _____

This container holds 1 quart.

Estimate how much each container holds. Then measure.

Container	Estimate	Measure
1	less than a quart more than a quart	less than a quart more than a quart
2	less than a quart more than a quart	less than a quart more than a quart
3	less than a quart more than a quart	less than a quart more than a quart
4	less than a quart more than a quart	less than a quart more than a quart

Copyright © SRA/McGraw-Hill.

 Note to Home Students estimate and measure capacity in quarts.

eTextbook This lesson is available in the *eTextbook*.

Ring the container that holds more.

5

6

7

8 **Extended Response** Chris needs to add 3 quarts of water to his aquarium. He has a 2-quart container and a 1-quart container. Draw a picture to show how he can get 3 quarts. Then draw a picture to show how he can do it another way.

Note to Home Students estimate capacity.

Name _____ Date _____

Listen to the problem.

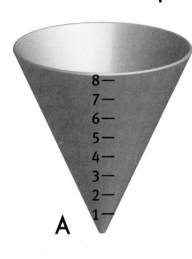

A

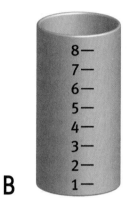

B

C

D

Which rain gauge will work the best?

_____

Why? _____

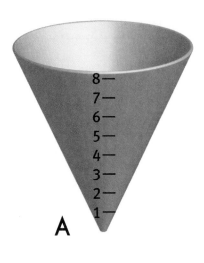

A

B

C

D

If it rains for an hour, in which gauge will the water be highest?

_____

If it rains for an hour, in which gauge will the water be lowest?

_____

Cumulative Review

Name _____ Date _____

Find the rule.

1

in	out
4	2
8	6
2	0
5	3

The rule is _____

2

in	out
1	1
9	9
5	5
7	7

The rule is _____

3

in	out
7	10
2	5
5	8
1	4

The rule is _____

4

in	out
2	3
8	9
5	6
7	8

The rule is _____

Cumulative Review

Adding Doubles 6–10 **Lesson 6.5**

Find the sums.

⑤ $10 + 10 =$ _____   **⑥** $2 + 2 =$ _____

⑦ $4 + 4 =$ _____   **⑧** $3 + 3 =$ _____

⑨ $1 + 1 =$ _____   **⑩** $0 + 0 =$ _____

Inequalities and Equalities II **Lesson 7.10**

Draw the right sign. Draw <, >, or =.

⑪ $12 + 2$ ◯ 14 **⑫** $12 + 1$ ◯ 14

⑬ 15 ◯ $9 + 3$ **⑭** 15 ◯ $9 + 4$

⑮ $8 + 8$ ◯ 16 **⑯** $8 + 7$ ◯ 16

Fractional Parts **Lesson 10.7**

Ring the fraction that relates to the picture.

⑰

$\frac{1}{2}$ $\frac{1}{3}$ $\frac{1}{4}$

⑱

$\frac{1}{2}$ $\frac{1}{3}$ $\frac{1}{4}$

⑲

$\frac{1}{2}$ $\frac{1}{3}$ $\frac{1}{4}$

Name _____ Date _____

Lessons 11.1–11.2 **Draw** the temperature.

1 40° Fahrenheit

2 50° Celsius

Lesson 11.4 **How** many centimeters? Use your ruler to find out.

3

_____

4

_____

5

_____

Lesson 11.7 **Ring** the object that weighs less than 5 pounds.

 6

Lessons 11.8–11.9 **Ring** the container that holds more.

7

8

9

10

11

Practice Test

Name _____ Date _____

Ring the temperature.

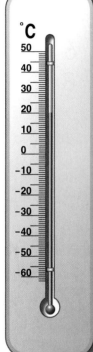

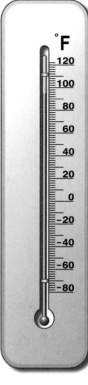

| **a.** 20 °C | **a.** 40 °C | **a.** 55 °F | **a.** 85 °F |
| **b.** 15 °C | **b.** 45 °C | **b.** 65 °F | **b.** 95° F |

a. 0 °C   **b.** 35 °C

a. 40 °F   **b.** 90 °F

Solve.

7 How many faces?

    a. 8
    b. 12
    c. 4
    d. 6

8 How many edges?

    a. 12
    b. 4
    c. 6
    d. 8

What fraction is shaded?

9

a. $\frac{1}{3}$ **b.** $\frac{1}{4}$

c. $\frac{1}{2}$ **d.** 1

10

a. $\frac{1}{3}$ **b.** $\frac{1}{4}$

c. $\frac{1}{2}$ **d.** 1

Which clock shows $\frac{1}{2}$ hour later?

11

a.   **b.**

c.   **d.**

12

a.   **b.**

c.   **d.**

Name _____ Date _____

Estimate.

⑬ Which one is less than 1 liter?

a. b. c. d.

⑭ Which one is more than 1 quart?

a. b. c. d.

⑮ Which one is less than 1 liter?

a. b. c. d.

⑯ Which one is less than 1 quart?

a. b. c. d.

(17) **Extended Response** Find height three different
ways. Fill in the chart. Use an object such as
a pencil or book. Use a ruler to measure
centimeters or meters. Use a ruler to
measure inches or feet.

	My Height	Height of a Partner
Object _____		
Centimeter Ruler		
Inch Ruler		

(18) **Extended Response** Which way works best to
measure your height? Say why you think so.

_____

_____

Manolita's
MAGNIFICENT MINUS
MACHINE

Decorate Manolita's Magnificent
Minus Machine.

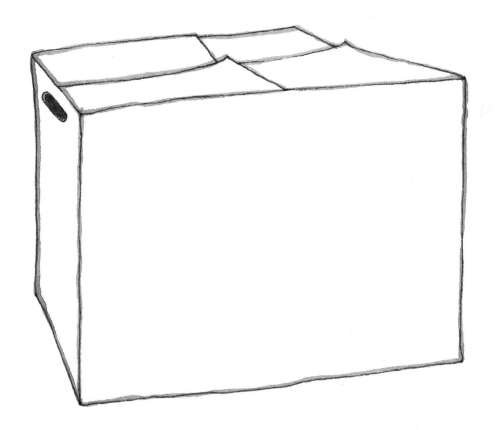

Note to Home Students listen to the Thinking Story "Manolita's
Magnificent Minus Machine" and answer questions about the story.

eTextbook This lesson is available in the *eTextbook*.

Ring how many of an item you will get back from Manolita's Magnificent Minus Machine.

You put in:

You put in:

You put in:

You put in:

In This Chapter You Will Learn

- about conventional numbers.
- two-digit addition and subtraction.

Name _____ Date _____

Draw a garden that has 100 squares.

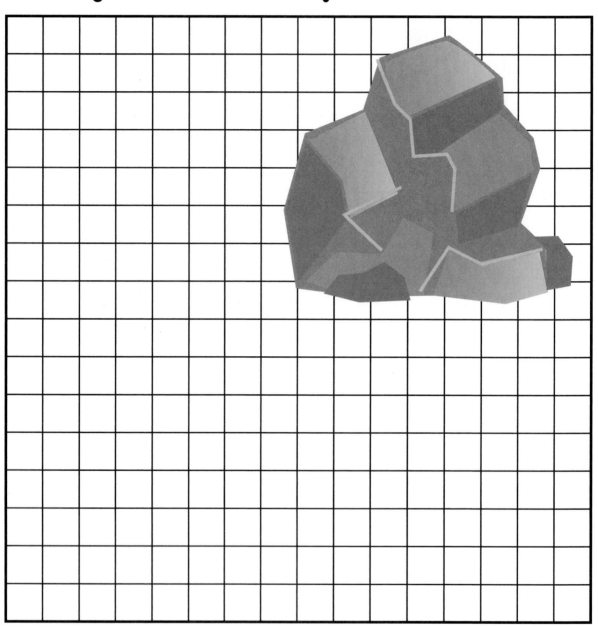

💡 **How do you know your garden has 100 squares?**

....

_____

LESSON 12.1 Reading and Writing Conventional Numbers

Ring the greater number or expression in each box.

1 | 28   81

2 | 46   71

3 | 62 + 1   52 + 2

4 | 22 − 3   22 − 4

Ring the greatest number or expression in each box.

5 | 17   26   21

6 | 15   8   31

7 | 17 + 2   17 + 4   17 + 5

8 | 85 − 1   85 − 3   95 − 10

Ring the lesser number or expression in each box.

9 | 33   26

10 | 87   54

11 | 48 + 3   49 + 3

12 | 62 − 1   52 − 1

Ring the least number or expression in each box.

13 | 17   9   52

14 | 56   77   49

15 | 83 + 5   83 + 1   82 + 1

16 | 29 − 1   29 − 3   29 − 10

Note to Home Students practice using conventional numbers.

Connect the dots. Start with 35 and count up.

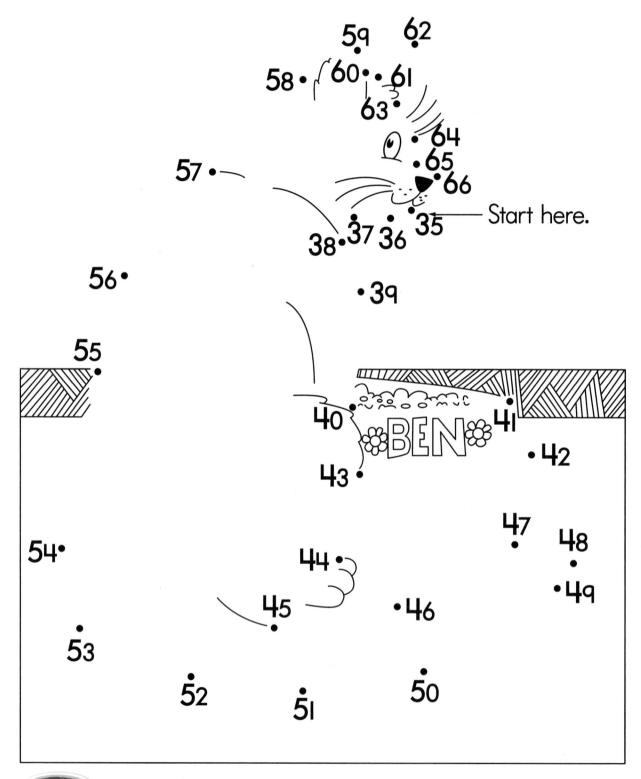

Start here.

Game Play the **Get to 100 by Tens or Ones Game.**

Note to Home Students use conventional numbers in a connect-the-dots activity.

424   **Real Math** · Chapter 12 · Lesson 1

LESSON 12.2 Skip Counting

Listen to the problems.

① _____ ② _____ ③ _____

Skip count to find the missing numbers.

4 | 2 | 4 | ___ | 8 | ___ | 12 | ___ | 16 | ___ | 20 |

5 2 + 2 + 2 + 2 + 2 = ___   **6** 2 + 2 + 2 + 2 = ___

7 | 3 | 6 | ___ | 12 | ___ | 18 | ___ | 24 | 27 |

8 3 + 3 + 3 = ___   **9** 3 + 3 + 3 + 3 + 3 = ___

10 | 4 | 8 | ___ | ___ | 20 | ___ | 28 | ___ | ___ | 40 |

11 4 + 4 + 4 + 4 = ___   **12** 4 + 4 + 4 + 4 + 4 = ___

Game Play the **Pattern Game.**

Note to Home Students use skip counting to find the missing numbers.

LESSON 12.3 **Arrays**

Listen to the problems.

1

_____

2

_____

3

_____

🎒 **Note to Home** Students solve word problems.

How many butterflies?

4 $4 + 4 =$ _____

5 $2 + 2 + 2 + 2 =$ _____

How many birds?

6 $5 + 5 + 5 =$ _____

7 $3 + 3 + 3 + 3 + 3 =$ _____

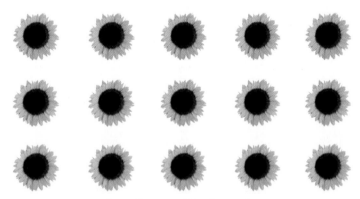

How many flowers?

8 $3 + 3 + 3 + 3 + 3 =$ _____

9 $5 + 5 + 5 =$ _____

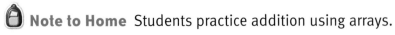 **Note to Home** Students practice addition using arrays.

Name _____ Date _____

LESSON 12.4 Using Bills

SOCIAL STUDIES **Listen** to the problems.

1 _____ **2** _____ **3** _____

How much money?

4

$ _____

5

$ _____

6

$ _____

7

$ _____

8

$ _____

9

$ _____

10

$ _____

 Play the **Yard Sale Game.**

 Note to Home Students find the total amount of money shown.

Name _____ Date _____

Solve these problems.

① One eraser costs 10¢. Fill in the chart so that it shows how much two, three, or more erasers will cost.

Number of Erasers	Cents
1	10
2	20
3	____
4	____
5	____
6	____
7	____

② How many erasers could you buy with 35¢? _____

How much would you have left over? _____ ¢

③ How many erasers could you buy with 18¢? _____

How much would you have left over? _____ ¢

④ How much would nine erasers cost? _____ ¢

🎒 **Note to Home** Students find given amounts of money.

Put a coin in each circle to make the correct amount. Write your answers.

5 25¢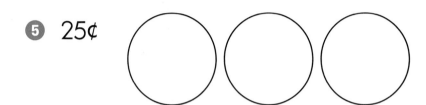

6 15¢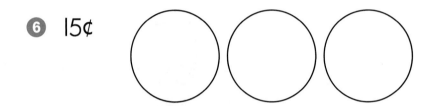

7 15¢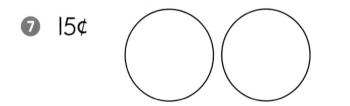

8 25¢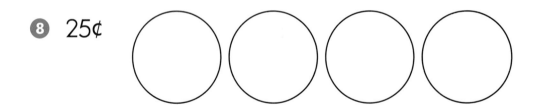

9 35¢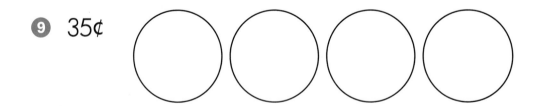

 Game Play the **School Bookstore Game.**

🎒 **Note to Home** Students make given amounts of money using coins.

LESSON 12.6 Introducing Quarters

How much money?

1

25¢ + 5¢ = _____ ¢

2

25¢ + 10¢ = _____ ¢

3

25¢ + 25¢ = _____ ¢

Use coins to help.

4 Make 35¢ with two coins.

5 Make 40¢ with four coins.

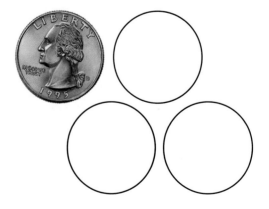

6 Make 45¢ with three coins.

Complete the chart. Use play coins if you need to.

Make this amount:	Use this coin:	How many coins?
$1		
$1		
50¢		
50¢		
25¢		
50¢		
$1		

Note to Home Students use coins to make different amounts of money.

Real Math • Chapter 12 • Lesson 6

LESSON 12.7 Counting by Fives and Tens

How many tally marks? Count by fives.
Then ring tens to check.

1. 卌 卌 卌 卌 卌 卌 卌 卌 卌 卌 卌   _____

2. 卌 卌 卌 卌 卌 卌 卌 卌   _____

3. 卌 卌 卌 卌 卌 卌 卌 卌 卌 卌 卌 卌   _____

4. 卌 卌 卌 卌 卌 卌 卌 卌 卌 卌 卌 || _____

5. 卌 卌 卌 卌 卌   _____

6. 卌 卌 卌 卌 卌 卌 卌 卌 卌 卌 ||| _____

Make the correct number of tally marks.
Then ring tens to show that you have
the correct number.

7. 20

8. 35

Note to Home Students use tally marks to count by fives and tens.

eTextbook This lesson is available in the *eTextbook*.

How many cents? Ring tens to check.

9

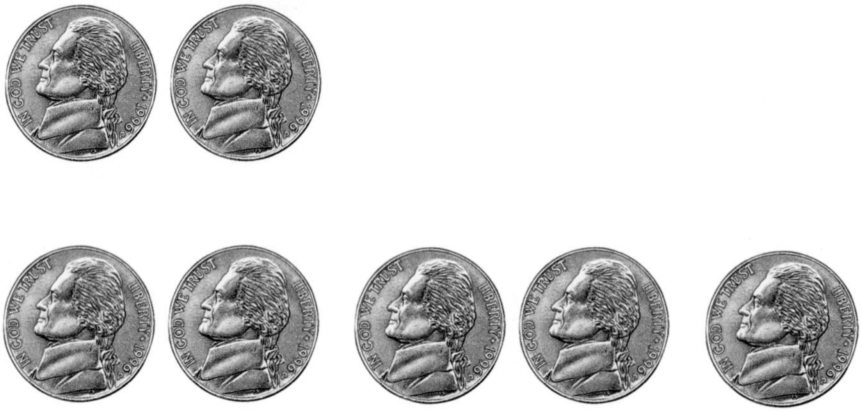

_____ ¢

10

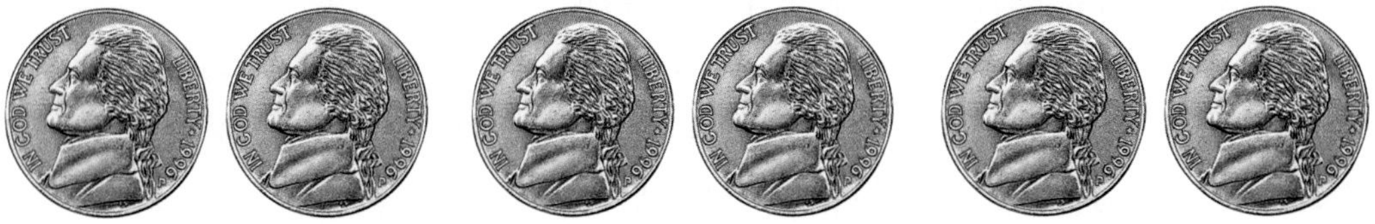

_____ ¢

11

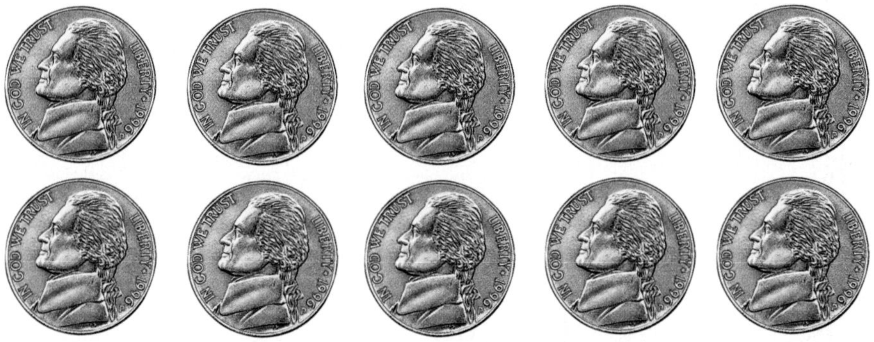

_____ ¢

12

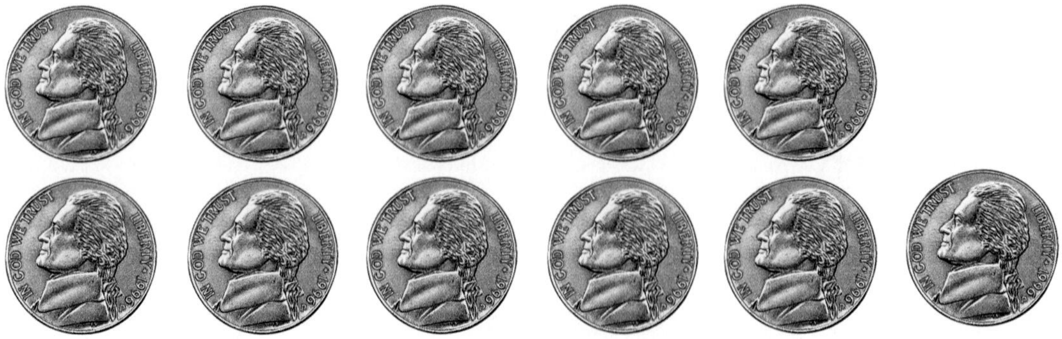

_____ ¢

Note to Home Students count coins.

Name _____ Date _____

Listen to the problem.

 Listen to the way Yung Su is solving the problem.

 Listen to the way Kaya is solving the problem.

How would you share the stickers?

For me: _____   For my friend: _____

Show how to share the stickers with a friend.

Show as many ways as you can.

For me	For my friend

Cumulative Review

Name _____ Date _____

Relating Addition and Subtraction I Lesson 7.3

Write the missing numbers.

1

	8
2	10

$8 + \underline{} = 12$

$12 - 8 = \underline{}$

Introducing Thirds and Fractions of Length Lesson 10.4

Ring the correct answer.

2

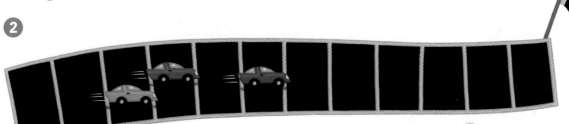

The green car is $\frac{1}{2}$ $\frac{1}{3}$ $\frac{1}{4}$ of the way to the finish line.

The red car is $\frac{1}{2}$ $\frac{1}{3}$ $\frac{1}{4}$ of the way to the finish line.

The blue car is $\frac{1}{2}$ $\frac{1}{3}$ $\frac{1}{4}$ of the way to the finish line.

Mental Subtraction Lesson 5.8

Do these in your head. Then write the answers.

3 $7 - 3 = \underline{}$

4 $7 - 1 = \underline{}$

Cumulative Review

Measuring Capacity in Liters Lesson 11.8

Ring the container that holds more.

5

6

7

Reading and Writing Conventional Numbers Lesson 12.1

Ring the greater number in each box.

8 | 28   81 |

9 | 46   71 |

Fractions on a Clock Lesson 10.8

10 What time is it? _____

What time will it be in half an hour?

_____

Mental Subtraction Lesson 5.8

Do these in your head. Then write the answers.

11 5 − 3 = _____   **12** 3 − 3 = _____   **13** 6 + 5 = _____

14 3 + 9 = _____   **15** 8 + 1 = _____   **16** 7 + 2 = _____

LESSON 12.8 Two-Digit Addition

Write how many. You may use sticks to help.

1 + + = ☐

2 + + + = ☐

3 38 + = ☐

4 38 + + = ☐

5 38 + 13 = ____

6 38 + 14 = ____

🎒 **Note to Home** Students use sticks to explore adding two-digit numbers.

ⓔ **Textbook** This lesson is available in the *eTextbook*.

441

Add. You may use manipulatives to help.

7 10 + 8 = _____

8 10 + 10 + 8 = _____

9 10 + 10 + 10 + 8 = _____

10 30 + 8 = _____

11 30 + 8 + 10 = _____

12 30 + 8 + 10 + 3 = _____

13 38 + 10 + 3 = _____

14 38 + 13 = _____

Note to Home Students use manipulatives to do addition exercises with two-digit numbers.

442   **Real Math** • Chapter 12 • Lesson 8

LESSON 12.9 More Two-Digit Addition

Listen to the story.

These students are using sticks to help find how many cookies were made.

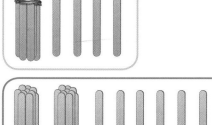

$$14 + 28 = \underline{}$$

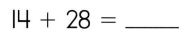

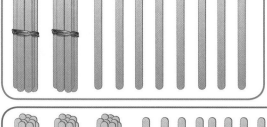

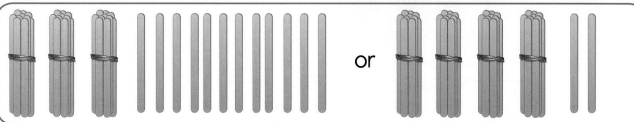

or

🎒 **Note to Home** Students use sticks to add two-digit numbers.

📖 **eTextbook** This lesson is available in the *eTextbook*.

443

Add. You may use sticks.

1 38 + 10 = _____

2 18 + 19 = _____

3 25 + 12 = _____

4 26 + 26 = _____

5 37 + 25 = _____

6 25 + 27 = _____

7 Andy found 18 rocks outside on Monday.
On Tuesday he found 35 more.
How many did he find altogether? _____

8 Jaime found 39 worms while she
was outside on Thursday. On Friday
she found 14 more worms.
How many did she find altogether? _____

🎒 **Note to Home** Students use craft sticks to add two-digit numbers.

LESSON 12.10 Two-Digit Subtraction

Listen to the story.

These students are using sticks to help find how many more students can go on the trip.

45 − 29 = _____

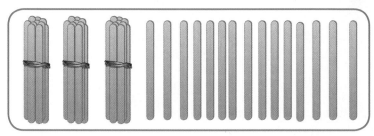

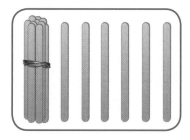

Note to Home Students use sticks to subtract two-digit numbers.

Subtract. You may use sticks.

1 45 − 20 = _____

2 45 − 23 = _____

3 35 − 17 = _____

4 51 − 22 = _____

5 38 − 20 = _____

6 38 − 19 = _____

7 Yesterday Victor had 44 seeds. Today he planted some. Now he has 18. How many did he plant? _____

🎒 **Note to Home** Students practice subtracting two-digit numbers.

Name _____ Date _____

Listen to the problem.

Draw your L-shaped garden.

Color four equal parts for four vegetables.

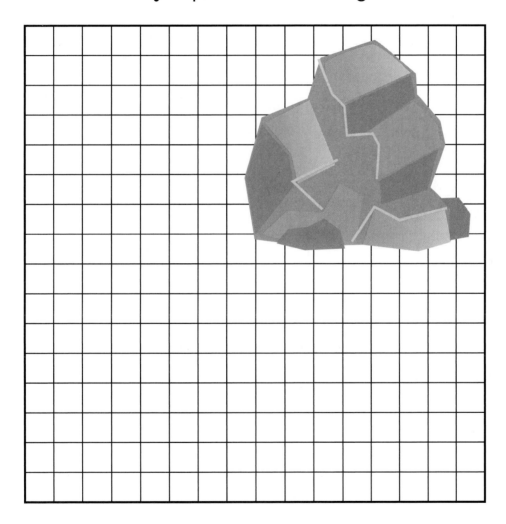

How many squares are in each part? _____

How did you solve the problem? _____

_____

Draw another garden.

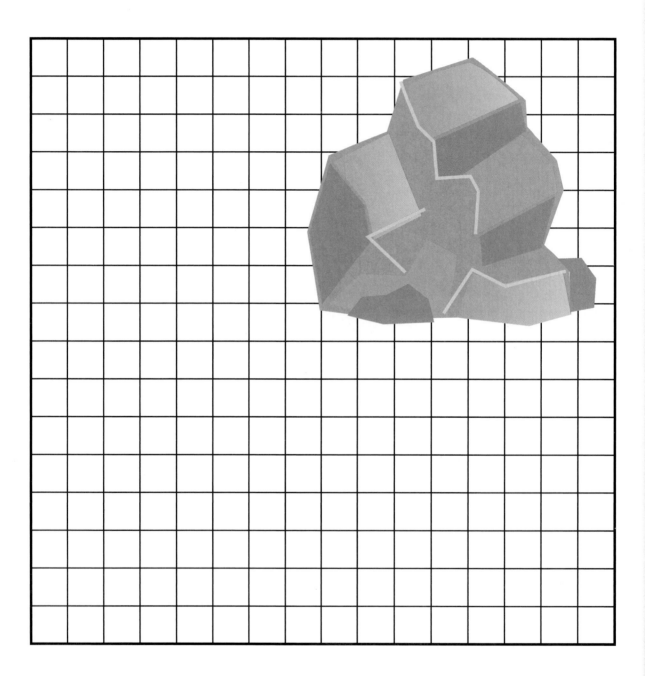

Cumulative Review

Name _____ Date _____

Numbers on a Clock Lesson 1.11

What time is it?

Adding and Subtracting (Vertical Form) Lesson 4.7

Listen to the problems. Solve.

4 Andrea has 6 red pencils and 2 blue pencils. How many pencils does she have?

_____

5 Michael has 5 pencils and 3 pens. How many pencils does he have?

_____

6 Erin had 6 pencils. Then she gave 2 of them to Keith. Now how many pencils does she have?

_____

Cumulative Review

Fractions and Multiples of Time **Lesson 10.9**

Listen to the problems.
Write the answers.

7 Travis can sing his favorite song in about 1 minute. How long would it take him to sing the song 4 times.

About _____ minutes.

8 Sumey colored 2 pictures. It took her about 1 hour. About how long would it take her to color 1 picture?

About _____ hour.

Chapter Review

Name _____ Date _____

Lessons 12.1 **Ring** the greater number or statement.

1 | 35   91 | **2** | 51 + 3   60 | **3** | 18   20 − 3 |

4 | 16 + 8   26 | **5** | 75 − 2   85 − 2 |

Lessons 12.2 **Skip** count to find the missing numbers.

6 $2 + 2 + 2 + 2 + 2 =$ _____

7 $4 + 4 + 4 + 4 + 4 + 4 + 4 =$ _____

8 $3 + 3 + 3 =$ _____

Lessons 12.3 **How** many flowers?

9 $3 + 3 + 3 + 3 =$ _____

10 $4 + 4 + 4 =$ _____

Lessons 12.4 **How** much money?

11  $ _____

12  $ _____

13  $ _____

Lessons 12.5 Put a coin in each circle to make the correct amount. Write numbers to show the coins you used.

14 35¢

◯ ◯ ◯ ◯

15 25¢

◯ ◯ ◯ ◯

Lessons 12.6 How much money?

16

$25¢ + 25¢ = \underline{\hspace{1cm}}¢$

17

$25¢ + 10¢ + 1¢ = \underline{\hspace{1cm}}¢$

Lessons 12.7 How many tally marks?
Count by fives. Then ring tens to check.

18 卌 卌 卌 卌 卌 卌 卌 卌 卌 卌 卌 || \underline{\hspace{1.5cm}}

19 卌 卌 卌 卌 ||| \underline{\hspace{1.5cm}}

20 卌 卌 卌 卌 卌 卌 卌 卌 卌 卌 卌 卌 卌 卌 卌 卌 \underline{\hspace{1.5cm}}

Lessons 12.8–8.10 Add or subtract.
You may use objects to help.

21 $48 + 13 = \underline{\hspace{1cm}}$

22 $65 - 30 = \underline{\hspace{1cm}}$

23 $18 + 36 = \underline{\hspace{1cm}}$

24 $64 - 12 = \underline{\hspace{1cm}}$

25 $22 + 59 = \underline{\hspace{1cm}}$

Name _____ Date _____

How many squares? Skip count to add.

1

$4 + 4 + 4 =$ _____

$3 + 3 + 3 + 3 =$ _____

2

$7 + 7 =$ _____

$2 + 2 + 2 + 2 + 2 + 2 + 2 =$ _____

How much money?

3

$ _____

4

_____ ¢

5

$ _____

6

_____ ¢

Ring the answer.

7 $\frac{1}{2}$ of 8 is _____

   a. 2   **b.** 8

   c. 16   **d.** 4

9 $\frac{1}{2}$ of 2 is _____

   a. 1   **b.** 2

   c. 4   **d.** 12

8 $\frac{1}{2}$ of 16 is _____

   a. 9   **b.** 8

   c. 32   **d.** 6

10 $\frac{1}{2}$ of 20 is

   a. 40   **b.** 10

   c. 20   **d.** 2

Ring the best answer.

11 Ring the one that weighs less than 50 pounds.

   a.

   b.

   c.

   d.

12 Ring the one that weighs more than 10 pounds.

   a.

   b.

   c.

   d.

Name _____ Date _____

Compare each number or statement.

13 Ring the greatest amount.

a. 50 + 4   **b.** 50 − 4
c. 50 + 1   **d.** 55 − 5

14 Ring the least amount.

a. 70 − 10   **b.** 20 + 60
c. 50 + 10   **d.** 60 − 10

Solve.

15 One pencil costs 5¢. How many can you buy with 30¢ ? _____

a. 4   **b.** 30   **c.** 6   **d.** 2

16 One pen costs 10¢. How many pens can you buy with 50¢ ? _____

a. 10   **b.** 5   **c.** 50   **d.** 3

Solve.

17 75 − 5 = 70
75 − 6 = _____

a. 76   **b.** 55   **c.** 69   **d.** 66

18 30 − 10 = 20
30 − 20 = _____

a. 10   **b.** 20   **c.** 50   **d.** 40

Practice Test

Add.

19 Add 43 + 34.
First make tens and ones.

$43 = 40 +$ _____

$34 =$ _____ $+ 4$

$40 +$ _____ $+$ _____ $+ 4 =$ _____

20 Add 61 + 25.
First make tens and ones.

$61 = 60 +$ _____

$25 = 20 +$ _____

$60 +$ _____ $+ 20 +$ _____ $=$ _____

21 **Extended Response** Add 33 + 33.
Find your own way. Show your work.

_____

_____   _____

22 **Extended Response** Add 46 + 16.
Find your own way. Show your work.

_____

_____   _____

Thinking Story

Trouble in the Garden

If the gardener grows all of the seeds, how many plants will she have? _____

CUCUMBERS 7 SEEDS

PUMPKIN 4 SEEDS

TOMATO PLANTS 3 SEEDS

GREEN BEANS 6 SEEDS

JALAPENOS 2 SEEDS

Note to Home Students listen to the Thinking Story "Trouble in the Garden" and answer questions about the story.

Textbook This lesson is available in the *eTextbook*.

Draw a picture of a plant with
seven leaves.

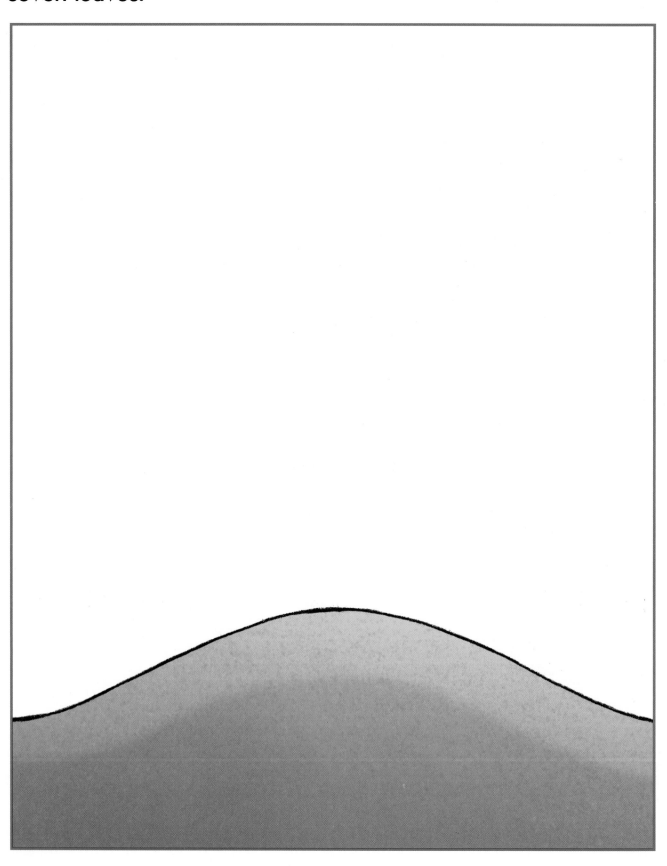

A

addition sentence

$$4 + 1 = 5$$

area

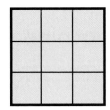

C

calendar

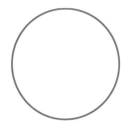

circle

clock

commutative law

$$2 + 3 = 5$$
$$3 + 2 = 5$$

cone

congruent

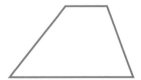

cube

Picture Glossary

D

difference

$$10 - 5 = \mathbf{5}$$

dime

dollar

E

equal

$$3 + 6 = 9$$

F

fourth

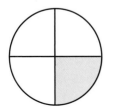

fraction

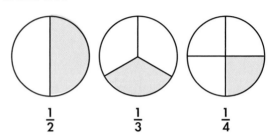

function machine

G

greater than

$$46 > 12$$

H

half

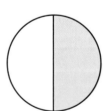

L

less than

$$10 < 65$$

460

N

nickel

Number Cube

number line

Number Strip

P

parallelogram

pattern

1 2 1 2 1 2

penny

perimeter

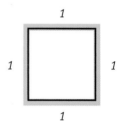

Q

quarter

Picture Glossary

R

rectangle

ruler

S

sphere

square

subtraction sentence

$$5 - 1 = 4$$

sum

$$4 + 2 = 6$$

symmetry

T

tally marks

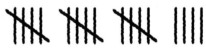

third

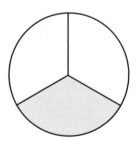

triangle

Cover Morgan-Cain & Associates; v, vii, ©PhotoDisc/Getty Images, Inc.; viii ©Aaron Haupt; ix ©Eyewire/Getty Images, Inc.; xiv ©PhotoDisc/Getty Images, Inc.;1 ©Stone/Getty Images, Inc.; 8, 9 ©Photo Disc/Getty Images, Inc.; 11 (tl) (bl) ©Matt Meadows, (tr) (br) ©Morton & White; 13, 14 ©PhotoDisc/Getty Images, Inc.; 17 (cl) (cr) ©PhotoDisc/Getty Images, Inc., (b) ©SRA Photos; 18 ©SRA Photo; 19 (t to b) ©PhotoDisc/Getty Images, Inc., ©Matt Meadows, ©PhotoDisc/Getty Images, Inc.; 20 ©PhotoDisc/Getty Images, Inc.; 21 (t to b) ©PhotoDisc/Getty Images, Inc., ©Morton & White, ©Stockbyte, ©PhotoDisc/Getty Images, Inc.; 22, 23 ©PhotoDisc/Getty Images, Inc.; 25 (t to b) ©PhotoDisc/Getty Images, Inc., ©Stockbyte; 31 ©PhotoDisc/Getty Images, Inc.; 32 (t to b) ©Morton & White, ©PhotoDisc/Getty Images, Inc., ©KS Studios, ©PhotoDisc/Getty Images, Inc.; 33, 34, 37- 41 ©PhotoDisc/Getty Images, Inc.; 47 ©Henny Ray Abrams/Reuters/CORBIS; 49 (t to b) ©PhotoDisc/Getty Images, Inc., ©Matt Meadows, ©JupiterImages Corporation/Comstock, Inc., ©PhotoDisc/Getty Images, Inc.; 50 (t to b) ©STONE/Getty Images, Inc., ©Digital Vision/Getty Images, Inc., ©The Image Bank/Getty Images, Inc., ©Dorling Kindersley/Getty Images, Inc.; ©Digital Vision/Getty Images, Inc.; 57 (t) ©PhotoDisc/Getty Images, Inc. (c) ©Mark M. Lawrence/CORBIS, (b) ©Stockbyte; 64 (l) ©PhotoDisc/Getty Images, Inc., (r) ©Matt Meadows; 65 ©SRA File; 67 ©Aaron Haupt; 73 (t) ©PhotoDisc/Getty Images, Inc., (c) ©Mark M. Lawrence/CORBIS; 81 ©AZURE COMPUTER & PHOTO SERVICES/AnimalsAnimals/Earth Scenes; 95-97 ©Matt Meadows; 98 (tc) (tr) ©RF/CORBIS, (tl) (tcl) (tc) (cl) (c) (cr) (bcl) (bcr) (br) ©PhotoDisc/Getty Images, Inc.; (bc) ©Stockbyte; 101 ©PhotoDisc/Getty Images, Inc.; 111 ©Jeff Christensen/Reuters/CORBIS; 128 ©PhotoDisc/Getty Images, Inc.; 130 ©Aaron Haupt; 132 ©Tom & Dee Ann McCarthy/CORBIS; 151 ©David/Young-Wolff/PhotoEdit, Inc.; 152, 153 ©Matt Meadows, ©SRA File; 155 ©Matt Meadows, (br) ©Aaron Haupt; 160 ©PhotoDisc/Getty Images, Inc.; 162 ©Eyewire/Getty Images, Inc.; 168, 169 ©PhotoDisc/Getty Images, Inc.; 170 ©Matt Meadows; 171, 172, 181 ©PhotoDisc/Getty Images, Inc.; 182, 183, 185 ©SRA File, ©Matt Meadows;191 ©Catherine Wessel/CORBIS; 194 ©Matt Meadows; 196; 209 (tr) ©Aaron Haupt; 211, 213 ©Matt Meadows; 218 ©PhotoDisc/Getty Images, Inc.; 226 ©Matt Meadows, ©SRA File; 233 ©SuperStock; 236 ©PhotoDisc/Getty Images, Inc.; 238 ©Eyewire/Getty Images, Inc.; 243 (tr) ©Tony Freeman/PhotoEdit, Inc.; 244 ©SuperStock; 249 (tr) ©Lawrence Manning/CORBIS; 251 ©PhotoDisc/Getty Images, Inc.; 262 (t) ©PhotoDisc/Getty Images, Inc., (c) ©Aaron Haupt; 271 ©Image Source/Getty Images, Inc.; 277 ©Matt Meadows, ©SRA File; 279, 281 ©Matt Meadows; 303 ©SRA File; 303, 308 ©Matt Meadows; 311 ©Bill Bachmann/PhotoEdit, Inc.; 315 ©PhotoDisc/Getty Images, Inc.; 317, 318 ©Matt Meadows; 323 (t) ©Phil Borden/PhotoEdit, Inc., (b) Navajo Rug, 29" x 48", woven by Nellie Klade of Chinle, Arizona in 2004. Photo courtesy, Hubbell Trading Post National Historic Site; 332 (tl) (2nd, 3rd row l-r) (bc) ©PhotoDisc/Getty Images, Inc., (tl) ©Aaron Haupt, (tr) ©Stefano Bianchetti/CORBIS, (tr) (bl) (br) ©Matt Meadows; 335 ©Matt Meadows; 337 ©Lonely Planet Images, Inc./Getty Images, Inc.; 342 (CW from top) (1), (2) (3) (4) (7) (8) ©PhotoDisc/Getty Images, Inc. (5) (6) ©Matt Meadows; 347 ©Matt Meadows; 349 ©The Image Bank/Getty Images, Inc.; 351, 355 ©PhotoDisc/Getty Images, Inc.; 361 (tr) ©STONE/Getty Images, Inc., (cl) ©Digital Vision/Getty Images, Inc., (cr) ©The Image Bank/Getty Images, Inc.; 362 ©Matt Meadows; 385 ©Hazir Reka/CORBIS; 393 ©PhotoDisc/Getty Images, Inc.; 395 (t) (b) ©PhotoDisc/Getty Images, Inc., (c) ©Morton & White; 399 ©PhotoDisc/Getty Images, Inc.; 401 (t) (c) ©PhotoDisc/Getty Images, Inc., (b) ©Morton & White; 402 (cl) (c) (bl) (b) (bc) (bcr) ©PhotoDisc/Getty Images, Inc., (tl) (tc) (cr) ©Matt Meadows; 404 (bc) ©SRA Photo, (tl) (c) (bl) ©Matt Meadows, (tc) (tr) (cl) (cr) (bcl) (br) ©PhotoDisc/Getty Images, Inc., (c) ©RF/CORBIS; 405- 408 ©Matt Meadows; 413 ©PhotoDisc/Getty Images, Inc.; 414 (tl) ©RF CORBIS, (tc) ©Matt Meadows, (tr) ©PhotoDisc/Getty Images, Inc., ©Matt Meadows; 417 © Eyewire/Getty Images, Inc., ©Matt Meadows, ©Morton & White, ©PhotoDisc/Getty Images, Inc.; 421 ©Jeff Greenberg/PhotoEdit, Inc.;426 ©PhotoDisc/Getty Images, Inc.; 428 (t) (b) ©PhotoDisc/Getty Images, Inc., (c) ©Roger Tidman/CORBIS; 430 ©Matt Meadows; 431(cr) ©Aaron Haupt; 433 ©Matt Meadows; 433, 434 ©SRA File; 436, 440 ©Matt Meadows; 442 ©PhotoDisc/Getty Images, Inc.; 443 ©Matt Meadows; 444(b) ©Aaron Haupt; 445 ©Matt Meadows; 446 ©PhotoDisc/Getty Images, Inc.; 451(cr) ©PhotoDisc/Getty Images, Inc., (b) ©Matt Meadows; 452, 453 ©SRA File, ©Matt Meadows.